28th edition

standard catalogue
of
Canadian coins

summer ~ 1979

FULLY ILLUSTRATED 1858 TO DATE
BY J.E. CHARLTON

INCLUDING

Grading Guide

An Historical Background of Canadian Coins,
Patterns, Essais, Commemorative Issues, Specimen Coins & Sets

Introductory Grading Guide

Commemorative Issues

Complete Illustrated Listing of
Canada's Silver & Gold Olympic Coins

Complete Mintage Figures

Latest Retail Values

THE STANDARD REFERENCE

published by

CHARLTON INTERNATIONAL
PUBLISHING INC.,
299 Queen Street West,
Toronto, Ontario.
M5V 1Z9

ISBN: 0-88968-002-7   *Printed in Canada*   *ISSN: 0706-0424*

TABLE OF CONTENTS

INTRODUCTORY

This Standard Catalogue (as the name implies) has set out to list, illustrate and price the principal types of coins which have served Canadian commerce. As a standard catalogue, it does not list - indeed, cannot - all the minor die varieties and other coinage variations that the specialist may find fascinating. These are specialized fields. A standard catalogue, in itself, however, offers liberal education in the numismatic lore of its country. The new reader very likely will find himself concentrating on the decimal coinage. With each return, he will approach the section with greater confidence, the various series, and their major varieties, fitting into place. Basic knowledge of these materials should add significance to articles that he reads and displays that he views.

Welcome, then, to Canada's Standard Catalogue - 28th edition - and, through it to the great breadth of Canadian numismatics. You'll find here the leads for a life-time of new interests, and new kinds of challenges to add zest to leisure hours. This carefully compiled volume reflects the co-ordinated contributions of many numismatic students, collectors, and dealers, over a full quarter century, and builds upon earlier scholarship of Canada's numismatic pioneers. In the longer, broader perspective of world numismatics, all this represents one chapter in a twenty-five century saga - but a remarkable chapter. Collect for enjoyment, for money is fascinating. This is an age of change and contrast. We've seen and spent a great variety of money. Significantly, as a future generation perhaps will acknowledge, there's not been a better or more interesting time than now to learn about money, to study it, and to collect.

NOTICE

The values quoted are based on the latest auction and retail prices. They are neither buying nor selling offers but give the most accurate appraisal of market values at the time of publication. In the case of some rare coins that seldom change hands, prices are subject to wide fluctuations between sales, so the author has listed the prices for the latest recorded sales.

PANEL OF CONTRIBUTORS

Walter Allan
H. Don Allen
G.H. Bishop
Al Bliman
Robert Byers
J. Lloyd Carney
Major Sheldon Carroll
John Cheramy
Freeman Clowery

William Cross
Peter Degraaf
Harry Eisenhauer
Allan Fargeon
J.D. Ferguson
R.P. Findlay
Vincent G. Greene
James Haxby
Leslie Hill

Gary Lazeo
Michael Levy
Barry Lipson
R.D. Lockwood
Lindsay McLennan
Charles Moore
J.A. Peddie
John Pittman
Myer Price

Douglas Robins
Michael Rogozinsky
Frank Rose
Royal Canadian Mint
Edmund Solski
Randy Weir

Credit is due the following for previous contributions:

*Fred Bowman, Kenneth E. Bresset, Melvin Came, Ronald Dickinson, John R. Francis, Jack L. Griffin, Walter Griggs, Thomas Grossman, Ray Hobin, F.E. Krumenacher, David Larson, William Lavell, *Robert A. Levy, *Maurice Lorrain, Jack & Beth Marles, C.F. Martin, Jack W. Olgilvie, *G.R.L. Potter, Joseph Powers, Fred Samuels, Neil Shafer, Harold Shaer, R.S. Shillingworth, Ingrid Smith, Cecil Tannahill, Sol Taylor, *Don Thomas, *Martin W. Watts, Terry Wedge, Robert C. Willey, R.S. Yeoman, Hans Zoell.

*deceased

FOREWARD

Some day, in the none to distant future, a spacesuited human may set foot on an arid, lifeless other world, perceive a glimmer in the dust, reach down, and claim an unprecedented prize - a metallic planchet, long lost "change", the first artifact of another civilization. It may not happen that way, of course, but there'll be irony if it does. Man's own past has sprinkled this world with coinage, each piece a record of a time and a place. Money, a remarkable abstraction, a unique invention, possesses a singular fascination for old and young. Accordingly, it is hardly surprising that the study and systematic collecting of monetary artifacts - coins, tokens, bank notes, even primitive monetary forms - is an enormously popular pastime and one that can be shown to date back for thousands of years.

Canada, by world standards, is a relatively youthful nation. Much settlement and development has taken place this century, and commerce as we know it is of comparatively recent origin. The monetary history of Canada is uncommonly rich and diverse, however, French colonial coinage and a fascinating series of jetons (counters) date from the period of New France, as of the remarkable "playing card" issues of emergency money. Fur traders used tokens to make change and facilitate trade, as did merchants in many pre-Confederation settlements. Bankers also issued tokens, and governments of several provinces circulated coins. Most present-day Canadian banks once issued their own paper money, as did scores of banks no longer in operation. When money or change was scarce, merchants might improvise their own paper scrip or tokens. Confederation saw introduction of Canadian government coinage and paper money, and Newfoundland released its own coins as late as 1947.

Recent years have seen a variety of attractive non-circulating coins in precious metals - silver and gold - struck to supplement Canada's present-day base-metal token coinage in bronze and nickel. Canadian monetary history will be seen to be so colourful and varied, and Canadian coinage, token and paper money series so attractive, interesting and challenging to study and collect, that it is hardly surprising that most coin enthusiasts in Canada specialize in Canadian material while a growing number of active collectors outside of Canada find a particular fascination in the money of this country.

NUMISMATICS — PAST AND PRESENT

Numismatics, in a traditional sense, is the study of coinage and of medallic art. Modern usage commonly extends the term to other monetary forms, the bank note, at its finest, being recognized as superb graphic art. The traditional numismatist likely was something of a classical scholar, his cabinet of type coins a record dating from Greece and Rome. The hobby undoubtedly is a venerable one; hoards of ancient coins have been unearthed that were essentially type collections. The present-day Canadian numismatist very likely was attracted to the hobby by one or both of two collecting areas, although his interest subsequently may have further developed and shifted or extended. He may have found fascination in the dated sequences of coins in pocket change or their older counterparts among family keepsakes. Or he may have been attracted by the beauty and prestige of senior denominations - silver dollars, Olympic silver, or older or modern gold. He may have sought a relaxing hobby, a hedge against inflation, or a "sure" speculation, but if he has persevered, and studied, and grown with his interest, he has added a new and improved dimension to his life.

Coin collecting has attracted a certain following in Canada for some generations but in terms both of interest and sheer numbers, recent years clearly reflect an all-time high. The late Victorian period and turn of the century witnessed a first peaking of interest in Canadian numismatics, with important works published and considerable enthusiasum for such Canadian "classics" as the bank and merchants' tokens. Then, for some decades, although interest in

United States series persisted, the number of Canadian collectors dropped markedly. Any major revival in Canadian numismatics awaited the years immediately following World War II. In 1950 collectors in the Ottawa area joined with scattered groups and individuals across the nation in forming the Canadian Numismatic Association. Annual conventions, duplicated Bulletins, and (from 1956) printed Journals served to bridge miles and to facilitate exchange of information and ideas. Canada's Standard Catalogue, then an unpretentious paperback with line drawings, tentative listings of tokens and coins, and a serious attempt at pricing, made its appearance in 1952, an immediate success and a significant addition to available numismatic literature. Its first expanded, hard-cover edition came out in 1960. Growth was rapid in organized numismatics in the 1950's. Coin clubs sprang up in cities and towns from coast to coast. Membership in the Canadian Numismatic Association reached the thousands, with collectors outside Canada, chiefly in the United States, discovering new interest in Canadian coins. Centennial coinage (special designs struck for circulation during Canada's centennial year), commemorative dollars, and Olympic silver and gold, also served to call attention to Canadian numismatic series. Whether the initial attraction was artistic, speculative, or interest in the theme, new collectors were added to the growing numbers who have learned to appreciate Canadian mintings.

AGE — RARITY — CONDITION - VALUE

Coins for collections can be obtained from mints and government agencies, from banks, from coin dealers, even from pocket change. Informal exchanging among collectors has a long tradition in the coin hobby. Changes in Canada's coinage in the 1960's, principally the replacing of silver pieces by nickel counterparts, has made collecting from circulation less of an adventure than once was the case. Older coins, in general, no longer circulate, and must be obtained from dealers and collectors or gleaned from family hoards. Coins no longer generally available take on numismatic values (as distinct from face values), values normally freely determined by factors of supply and demand.

"Rare" coins have built up about them a certain folklore, very often not wholly rooted in fact. The most famous of such charismatic coins no doubt is the 1804 silver dollar of the United States, but the search for a few such Canadian pieces has produced far more eyestrain than fortunes. The best examples are Canada's silver 5-cent and 50-cents of the 1921 issue, few of which entered active circulation and the "dot" cent and 10-cents of 1936. Fabulous prices have been paid at numismatic auctions for the few known genuine items, typically from specimen sets. Many lesser rarities, however, represent a distinct challenge to the persevering collector, to locate, acquire, and add to his or her basic collection. Value, the reader will note, is very much a function of condition. Many relatively common coins are hard to find in choice preservation, and pricing tends to reflect this fact of supply and demand. Collectors have developed a specializing vocabulary for describing the condition of a coin, giving definite meaning to terms such as "very good" and "extremely fine". Since condition is so vital in determining the value of a coin, attention must be directed to these standards. "Grading" of an individual coin tends to be less than a science, a subjective element very often entering in. A clear grasp of generally accepted grading criteria should do much to minimize misunderstanding, nonetheless.

DECIMAL COINAGES

Coins as Canadians now know them, date, in a sense, from the years prior to Confederation. The Province of Canada adopted "decimal" currency, a dollar of one hundred cents, in 1858, initial decimal coinage being struck in 1858 and 1859. The first denominations were 1-cent, 5-cents, 10-cents, and 20-cents. Additional silver 5-cent and 10-cent pieces were struck for the Dominion of Canada in 1870, continuing the same designs, and 25-cent and 50-cent pieces were introduced. Large cents were struck for the Dominion in 1876, in the 1880's and each year from 1890 to 1920, when the now familiar cent was introduced. "Fishscales", the undersized silver 5-cent pieces, were replaced by nickel coins in 1922. Canada's silver dollar first was struck for circulation in 1935, commemorating the silver anniversary of the reign of King George V and Queen Mary. Dollar coins have been struck each year since 1945. Gold was struck early in the century, then subsequently in Centennial and Olympic years and for the Silver Jubilee of Queen Elizabeth II. Canadian coins have portrayed five reigning sovereigns, Queen Victoria, Kind Edward VII, King George V, King George VI, and Queen Elizabeth II. No Canadian coins were issued in the name of King Edward VIII, although, as Prince of Wales, Edward was featured on several issues of notes.

Each of the Maritime Provinces decimalized its currency during the period prior to Confederation, and coins struck for these provinces remained in circulation for many years. Newfoundland decimalized in 1865, issuing bronze cents; 5, 10 and 20-cent pieces in silver; and a $2 piece in gold. A 50-cent piece was introduced in 1870, and 25-cent coins were struck in 1917 and 1919. Newfoundland coins have been deservedly popular for many years. Small strikings and interesting varieties make all series challenging and rewarding to collect.

Curiously, despite efforts to expand its range, Canadian coinage has tended to emphasize four, and only four, denominations. The bronze cent ("penny" is a misnomer; "copper" an anachronism) serves as least common denominator in all commerce, though in itself it will buy little. No fractional coinage has been struck since Confederation (Nova Scotia issued half cents), nor have fractional tax tokens seen Canadian use. Five-cent pieces have been struck in silver, pure nickel and other metallic compositions, and long were called "nickels" being Canada's only nickel coin. Ten-cent and twenty-five-cent pieces were Canada's traditional "silver" and now are pure nickel. ("Dime" and "quarter dollar", of course, are Americanisms, inappropriate in Canadian numismatic use). Fifty-cent pieces and dollar coins have had limited general circulation. Fifties enjoyed popularity in Newfoundland and some other regions. Dollars traditionally have been presentation pieces, a gift (for a silver anniversary, possibly) that quickly found its way back to the bank.

Olympic silver and gold, Centennial and Commemorative gold, and later dollar releases in silver, have been declared legal tender, and so could be spent as money, but in fact never were. Available only at a premium over face value (legal tender value), their spending would have involved substantial loss so their only use was as collector's items and memorabilia. Some collectors carefully avoid such non-circulating coins. Others accept them readily, as investments or as outstanding examples of medallic art.

CANADIAN COMMEMORATIVES

A group of coins of considerable international interest comprises Canadian commemoratives struck for general circulation. Most silver dollars were in this category, at least in the sense that they were freely available at face value to those who wanted to save or spend them. Other such commemoratives are the 1951 5-cent piece, marking the anniversary of the isolation of the metal nickel, the 1967 Centennial coins, and the 1973 25-cents, honouring the Royal Canadian Mounted Police.

MINTS AND MINT MARKS

A variety of letters and numerals are to be found on Canadian coins and collectors frequently are asked their significance. Mint marks, used to designate the minting facilities at which coins were struck, reflect a venerable tradition. Unlike most United States coins, on which D for Denver and S for San Francisco are readily found, most Canadian coins do not bear mint marks, the few that do being the more interesting for it. Canadian coinage struck prior to 1908 was produced at the Tower Mint, London, and bears no mint mark - apart from strikings subcontracted to The Mint, Birmingham (Heaton's Mint) which are identified by mint mark H. Coins struck at Canadian minting facilities (since 1908) in general do not bear mint marks, exceptions being gold sovereigns (mint mark C) and certain Newfoundland coinage (also mint mark C). Certain Canadian 10-cent nickel coins of 1968 were struck at the main United States Mint, Philadelphia. These carry neither the P mint mark nor the "Made in U.S.A." normally required on imported tokens, but are readily identified by collectors due to the American style reeding (grooves) on the edges. Other initials on coins (normally somewhat smaller than mint marks) serve to identify designers. Those found on Canadian coins include:

B.M. . . . . Sir Bertram MacKennal	M.G. . . . . Mrs. Mary Gillick
P.M. . . . . Percy Metcalfe	P.P . . . . Paul Pederson
B.P . . . . Benedetto Pistrucci	D.D.P. . . . . .Donald D. Patterson
D.E.S. . . . . .G.W. DeSaulles	R.T . . . . .Raymond Taylor
D.V . . . . Dinko Vodanovic	T.M . . . . Terry Manning
E.H . . . . .Emmanuel Hahn	S.T . . . . Stephen Trenka
H.P . . . . Humphrey Paget	T.S . . . . .Thomas Shingles
K.G. . . . . Kruger Gray	W.W. . . . . William Wyon
L.C.W. or L.W. . . . . . . Leonard C. Wyon	P.B. . . . . Patrick Brindley
P.C . . . . .Paul Cedarberg	

BUILDING A COLLECTION

Collecting is a highly individual matter. Each collector is free to make his own rules as to the materials he will seek, the condition he will require, and the manner in which he will organize and house his collection. One caveat is indicated: the collector concerned about resale value of his "holdings" (and most are, to a degree) will be wise to bear in mind that best prices tend to be paid for items and conditions in greatest demand; that is, for best returns, he would do well to follow, even anticipate, general trends in collecting. However, there can be no question that much of the most interesting Canadian numismatic material currently is a part of the mainstream of demand, and that many earlier items, of some scarcity, can be acquired and enjoyed at relatively modest expenditure.

The traditional coin cabinet of numismatics has largely given way to a diversity of cardboard and plastic coin holders, coin albums and other imaginative storage facilities. For reasons of security, most serious collectors keep their choicest materials in bank vaults.

FRATERNAL AFFILIATION

Coin clubs have developed in many Canadian communities and the fraternal, educational side is one of the most attractive features of present-day collecting. New clubs are organizing, and established groups usually can be counted upon for encouragement and support. Larger centres have periodic coin shows which afford opportunity to meet other collectors and to examine educational displays. Conventions of national and international stature are held annually by the Canadian Numismatic Association, American Numismatic Association, and by regional and specialized groups.

Major numismatic associations publish journals, maintain lending libraries (accessible by mail), organize meetings, and generally support the collecting interests of their members. Two such organizations of interest to Canadian collectors and students of Canadian numismatics are:

Canadian Numismatic Association, Post Office Box 226, Barrie, Ont. Canada L4M 4T2	American Numismatic Association, Post Office Box 2366, Colorado Springs, Col. 80901

The A.N.A. is the world's largest such organization and its unequelled resources always have been accessible to Canadians.

Another organization of particular interest to professional numismatists has come into being. All inquiries should be addressed to:

Executive Secretary
The Canadian Association of Numismatic Dealers
Post Office Box 3145, Station 'D',
Willowdale, Ontario.

CONDITION OF COINS

The first listing of grading standards for Canadian coins appeared in the 1952 Charlton Catalogue, and this has been considerably enlarged and refined in the intervening years.

However, with the American Numismatic Association adopting the numerical grading system, it was felt that a similar system should be considered for use in Canadian numismatics.

After much deliberation and compilation of the results of an extensive survey conducted by the author, the decision has been made to adopt the A.N.A.'s "Official Grading System" for use in this the 28th edition of the Charlton Standard Catalogue of Canadian Coins.

The following text and the Official Grading System has been reproduced with the express permission of the American Numismatic Association.

WHY IS GRADING IMPORTANT?

Why are there differences of opinion in the field of grading coins? There are numerous reasons, but the most common are as follows:

Grading coins can never be completely scientific in all areas. One may weigh a coin and also obtain its specific gravity by mechanical devices, and the results will be factual if accurate equipment was used carefully. There are no scientific means available to measure the surface condition - the amount of wear - of a coin.

In grading coins, considerations such as striking, surface of the planchet, the presence of heavy toning (which may obscure certain surface characteristics), the design, and other factors each lend an influence. A panel containing a dozen of the foremost numismatic hobby leaders justifiably could have some slight differences of opinion on the precise grade of some coins.

However, it is not slight differences which concern us here; it is serious or major differences. The term "overgrading" refers to describing a coin as a grade higher than it actually is. For example, if a coin in AU (About Uncirculated) is called Uncirculated, it is overgraded. If a coin in Very Fine grade is called Extremely Fine, it is overgraded.

What induces overgrading? Here are some of the factors:

Buyers Seeking Bargains. The desire to get a bargain is part of human nature. If a given Uncirculated coin actively traded at $100 is offered at $70, it will attract a lot of bargain seekers. These same buyers would reject an offering such as: "I am offering this stock, which trades on the New York Stock Exchange for $100, for just $70 cash," or "I am offering $100 bills for $70 each."

In coins, as in any other walk of life, you get what you pay for. If a coin which has a standard value of $100 is offered for $70 there may be nothing wrong, but chances are that the piece is overgraded.

False Assumptions. Buyers often assume falsely that any advertisement which appears in a numismatic publication has been approved by that publication. Actually, publishers cannot be expected to examine coins and approve of all listing offered. A person who has no numismatic knowledge or expertise whatsoever can have letterheads and business cards printed and, assuming he has good financial and character references (but not necessarily numismatic expertise), run large and flashy advertisements. Months or years later it is often too late for the deceived buyer to get his money back. The solution to this is to learn how to grade coins and think for yourself. Examine the credentials of the seller. Is he truly an expert in his field? To what professional organization does the dealer belong? It is usually foolish to rush and spend your hard earned money with a coin seller who has no professional credentials and whose only attraction is that he is offering "bargains." Think for yourself!

The Profit Motive. Sellers seeking an unfair markup may overgrade. For purposes of illustration, let us assume that a given variety of coin is worth the following prices in these grades: AU $75, and Uncirculated $150. A legitimate dealer in the course of business would buy, for example, an AU coin at $50 or $60 and sell it retail for $75, thus making a profit of $15 to $25. However, there are sellers who are not satisfied with the normal way of doing business. They take shortcuts. They pay $50 or $60 for the same AU coin which is worth $75 retail, but rather than calling it AU they call it "Uncirculated" and sell it for $150. So, instead of making $15 or $25 they make $90 to $100!

Inexperience. Inexperience or error on the part of the seller may lead to incorrect grading - both overgrading and undergrading.

PROOF COINS

The term "proof" refers to a manufacturing process which results in a special surface or finish on coins made for collectors. Most familiar are modern brilliant proofs. These coins are struck at the mint by a special process. Carefully prepared dies, sharp in all features, are made. Then the flat surfaces of the dies are given a high mirror-like polish. Specially prepared planchets are fed into low-speed coining presses. Each proof coin is slowly and carefully struck more than once to accentuate details. When striking is completed the coin is taken from the dies with care and not allowed to come into contact with other pieces. The result is a coin with mirror-like surface. The piece is then grouped together with other denominations in a set and offered for sale to collectors.

Additional Points Concerning Proofs: Certain regular issues or business strike coins have nearly full proof-like surfaces. These were produced in several ways. Usually regular issue dies (intended to make coins for circulation) were polished to remove surface marks or defects for extended use. Coins struck from these dies were produced at high speed, and the full proof surface is not always evident. Also, the pieces are struck on ordinary planchets. Usually such pieces, sometimes called "first strikes" or "proof-like Uncirculated", have patches of Uncirculated mint frost. A characteristic in this regard is the shield on the reverse (on coins with this design). The features within the design on proofs are fully brilliant, but on proof-like non-proofs they usually are not mirror-like. Also, the striking may be weak in areas and the rims might not be sharp.

The mirror-like surface of a brilliant proof coin is much more susceptible to damage than are the surfaces of an Uncirculated coin. For this reason, proof coins which have been cleaned often show a series of fine hairlines or minute striations. Also, careless handling has resulted in certain proofs acquiring marks, nicks and scratches.

SPECIMENS are quite similar to Proofs and often referred to as Proofs, but prior to 1976 the Ottawa Mint used the term Specimen, which is of slightly lesser quality, for their presentation coin sets. Brilliant Specimens have a brilliant mirror-like surface like the 1967 Centennial gold set. Matte Specimens have a granular sandblast surface, like the majority of 1908, 1911 and 1937 cased sets.

Proofs are divided into the following classifications:

Proof-70 (Perfect Proof). A Proof-70 or Perfect Proof is a coin with no hairlines, handling marks, or other defects; in other words, a flawless coin. Such a coin may be brilliant or may have natural toning.

Proof-65 (Choice Proof). Proof-65 or Choice Proof refers to a proof which may show some very fine hairlines, usually from friction-type cleaning or friction-type drying or rubbing after dipping. To the unaided eye, a Proof-65 or a Choice Proof will appear to be virtually perfect. However, 5x magnification will reveal some minute lines. Such hairlines are best seen under strong incandescent light.

Proof-60 (Proof). Proof-60 refers to a proof with some scattered handling marks and hairlines which will be visible to the unaided eye.

Impaired Proofs; Other Comments. If a proof has been excessively cleaned, has many marks, scratches, dents or other defects, it is described as an impaired proof. If the coin has seen extensive wear then it will be graded one of the lesser grades - Proof-55, Proof-45, or whatever. It is not logical to describe a slightly worn proof as "AU" (Almost Uncirculated) for it never was "Uncirculated" to begin with - in the sense that Uncirculated described a top grade normal production strike. So, the term "impaired proof" is appropriate. It is best to describe fully such a coin, examples being: "Proof with extensive hairlines and scuffing", or "Proof with numerous nicks and scratches in the field", or "Proof-55 with light wear on higher surfaces".

UNCIRCULATED COINS

The term "Uncirculated", interchangeable with "Mint State", refers to a coin which has never seen circulation. Such a piece has no wear of any kind. A coin as bright as the time it was minted or with very little light natural toning can be described as "Brilliant Uncirculated". A coin which has natural toning can be described as "Toned Uncirculated". Except in the instance of copper coins, the presence or absence of light toning does not affect an Uncirculated coin's grade. Indeed, among silver coins, attractive natural toning often results in the coin bringing a premium.

The quality of lustre or "mint bloom" on an Uncirculated coin is an essential element in correctly grading the piece, and has a bearing on its value. Lustre may in time become dull, frosty, spotted or discoloured. Unattractive lustre will normally lower the grade.

With the exception of certain Special Mint Sets made in recent years for collectors, Uncirculated or normal production strike coins were produced on high speed presses, stored in bags together with other coins, run through counting machines, and in other ways handled without regard to numismatic posterity. As a result, it is the rule and not the exception for an Uncirculated coin to have bag marks and evidence of coin-to-coin contact, although the coin might not have actual commercial circulation. The amount of such marks will depend upon the coin's actual size. Differences in criteria in this regard are given in the individual sections under grading descriptions for different denominations and types.

Uncirculated coins can be divided into three major categories:

MS-70 (Perfect Uncirculated). MS-70 or Perfect Uncirulcated is the finest quality available. Such a coin under 4x magnification will show no bag marks, lines, or other evidence of handling or contact with other coins.

A brilliant coin may be described as "MS-70, Brilliant" or "Perfect Brilliant Uncirculated". A lightly toned nickel or silver coin may be described as "MS-70, toned" or "Perfect Toned Uncirculated". Or, in the case of particularly attractive or unusual toning, additional adjectives may be in order such as "Perfect Uncirculated with attractive iridescent toning around the borders".

Copper and bronze coins: To qualify as MS-70 or Perfect Uncirculated, a copper or bronze coin must have its full lustre and natural surface colour, and may not be toned brown, olive, or any other colour. (Coins with toned surfaces which are otherwise perfect should be described as MS-65 as the following text indicates).

MS-65 (Choice Uncirculated). This refers to an above average Uncirculated coin which may be brilliant or toned (and described accordingly) and which has fewer bag marks than usual; scattered occasional bag marks on the surface or perhaps one or two very light rim marks.

MS-60 (Uncirculated). MS-60 or Uncirculated (typical Uncirculated without any adjectives) refers to a coin which has a moderate number of bag marks on its surface. Also present may be a few minor edge nicks and marks, although not of a serious nature. Unusually deep bag marks, nicks and the like must be described separately. A coin may be either brilliant or toned.

Striking and Minting Peculiarities on Uncirculated Coins

Certain early coins have mint-caused planchet or adjustment marks, a series of parallel striations. If these are visible to the naked eye they should be described adjectivally in addition to the numerical or regular descriptive grade. For example: "MS-60 with adjustment marks", or "MS-65 with adjustment marks", or "Perfect Uncirculated with very light adjustment marks", or something similar.

If an Uncirculated coin exhibits weakness due to striking or die wear, or unusual (for the variety) die wear, this must be adjectivally mentioned in addition to the grade. Examples are: "MS-60, lightly struck", or "Choice Uncirculated, lightly struck", and "MS-70, lightly struck".

CIRCULATED COINS

Once a coin enters circulation it begins to show signs of wear. As time goes on the coin becomes more and more worn until, after a period of many decades, only a few features may be left.

Dr. William H. Sheldon devised a numerical scale to indicate degrees of wear. According to this scale, a coin in condition 1 of "Basal State" is barely recognizable. At the opposite end, a coin touched by even the slightest trace of wear (below MS-60) cannot be called Uncirculated.

While numbers from 1 through 59 are continuous, it has been found practical to designate specific intermediate numbers to define grades. Hence, this text uses the following descriptions and their numerical equivalents:

Choice About Uncirculated-55. Abbreviation: AU-55. Only a small trace of wear is visible on the highest points of the coin. As is the case with the other grades here, specific information is listed in the following text under the various types, for wear often occurs in different spots on different designs.

About Uncirculated-50. Abbreviation: AU-50. With traces of wear on nearly all of the highest areas. At least half of the original mint lustre is present.

Choice Extremely Fine-45. Abbreviation: EF-45. With light overall wear on the coin's highest points. All design details are very sharp. Mint lustre is usually seen only in protected areas of the coin's surface.

Extremely Fine-40. Abbreviation: EF-40. With only slight wear but more extensive than the preceeding, still with excellent overall sharpness. Traces of mint lustre may still show.

Choice Very Fine-30. Abbreviation: VF-30. With light even wear on the surface; design details on the highest points lightly worn, but with all lettering and major features sharp.

Very Fine-20. Abbreviation: VF-20. As preceeding but with moderate wear on highest parts.

Fine-12. Abbreviation: F-12. Moderate to considerable even wear. Entire design is bold. All lettering visible, but with some weaknesses.

Very Good-8. Abbreviation: VG-8. Well worn. Most fine details such as hair strands, leaf details, and so on are worn nearly smooth.

Good-4. Abbreviation: G-4. Heavily worn. Major designs visible, but with faintness in areas. Other major features visible in outline form without centre detail.

About Good-3. Abbreviation: AG-3. Very heavily worn with portions of the lettering, date, and legends being worn smooth. The date is barely readable.

Note: The exact descriptions of circulated grades vary widely from issue to issue, so the preceeding commentary is only of a very general nature.

SPLIT AND INTERMEDIATE GRADES

It is often the case that because of the peculiarities of striking or a coin's design, one side of the coin will grade differently from the other. When this is the case, a diagonal mark is used to separate the two. For example, a coin with an AU-50 obverse and a Choice Extremely Fine-45 reverse can be described as: AU/EF or, alternatively, 50/45.

The A.N.A. standard numerical scale is divided into the following steps: 3, 4, 8, 12, 20, 30, 45, 50, 55, 60, 65, and 70. Most advanced collectors and dealers find that the graduations from AG-3 through Choice AU-55 are sufficient to describe nearly every coin showing wear. The use of intermediate grade levels such as EF-42, EF-43, and so on is not encouraged. Grading is not that precise, and using such finely split intermediate grades is imparting a degree of accuracy which probably will not be able to be verified by other numismatists. As such, it is discouraged.

A split or intermediate grade, such as that between VF-30 and EF-40, should be called Choice VF-35 rather than VF-EF or About EF.

An exception to intermediate grades can be found among Mint State coins, coins grading from MS-60 through MS-70. Among Mint State coins there are fewer variables. Wear is not a factor; the considerations are the amount of bag marks and surface blemishes. While it is good numismatic practice to adhere to the numerical classifications of 60, 65, and 70, it is permissible to use intermediate grades.

In all instances, the adjectival description must be of the next lower grade. For example, a standard grade for a coin is MS-60 or Uncirculated Typical. The next major category is MS-65 or Uncirculated Choice. A coin which is felt to grade, for example, MS-64, must be described as "MS-64, Uncirculated Typical". It may not be described as Choice Uncirculated, for the minimum definition of Choice Uncirculated is MS-65. Likewise, an MS-69 coin must be described as: MS-69, Uncirculated Choice. It is not permissible to use Uncirculated Perfect for any coin which is any degree less than MS-70.

The A.N.A. grading system considers it to be good numismatic practice to adhere to the standard 60, 65, and 70 numerical designations. Experienced numismatists can generally agree on whether a given coin is MS-60 or MS-65. However, not even the most advanced numismatists can necessarily agree on whether a coin is MS-62 or MS-63; the distinction is simply too minute to permit accuracy. In all instances, it is recommended that intermediate grades be avoided, and if there is any doubt, the lowest standard grade should be used. The use of plus or minus signs is also not acceptable practice.

We wish to take this opportunity to express our appreciation to the American Numismatic Association for allowing us to use their Official Grading System in this catalogue.

OBVERSE UNCIRCULATED, MS-60 — There should be absolutely no wear of any kind on the hair and diadem. There may be a nick, a few bag marks or some discoloration but a high degree of lustre or frost should remain.
REVERSE UNCIRCULATED, MS-60 — All detail in the wreath, crown and bow are sharp and maple boughs clearly defined.

OBVERSE ABOUT UNCIRCULATED, AU-50 — Very slight traces of wear on diadem and in hairlines but details still sharp. Half of mint lustre remaining.
REVERSE ABOUT UNCIRCULATED, AU-50 — Slight trace of wear on high points - knot in wreath, crown and lower leaves.

OBVERSE EXTREMELY FINE, EF-40 — Trace of wear on eyebrow, four jewels in rim of diadem, strands of hair over the ear, knot at back and hairlines on top of head.
REVERSE EXTREMELY FINE, EF-40 — Trace of wear around the outer edges of lower leaves, knot in wreath and crown.

OBVERSE VERY FINE, VF-20 — Slight wear on eyebrow, cheek, nose, ear lobe and all of the jewels. Ribbon end on neck begins to merge. Hair over the ear and knot slightly worn.
REVERSE VERY FINE, VF-20 — All leaves show wear on outer edges. Knot in wreath and centre part of crown worn.

OBVERSE FINE, F-12 — Considerable wear on all facial features, also hair and jewels. Ribbon end fused with cheek. Strands of hair over the ear begin to merge together. Ear lobe barely showing.
REVERSE FINE, F-12 — All leaves considerably worn ever entire area, also crown. Pearls in crown and beads of border begin to merge.

OBVERSE VERY GOOD, VG-8 — Ear lobe fused with cheek. Hairlines separating face from hair obliterated. Practically no details in hair over ear and knot at back. Jewels mostly worn away.
REVERSE VERY GOOD, VG-8 — Very little detail in the leaves and crown remain. Border beads are blurred. Value and date are worn.

OBVERSE GOOD, G-4 — Details of jewels, diadem and hair are worn off. Little but outline of portrait remains. Legend is weak.
REVERSE GOOD, G-4 — Leaves and crown badly worn, with little but outlines remaining. Value and date are weak. Border beads are blurred.

Note: The 50¢ coins have been used to illustrate grading conditions as they are most representative of the Canadian coinage.

OBVERSE UNCIRCULATED, MS-60 — Robe, shoulder bow, crown, ear and side whiskers all show sharp detail. All jewels in the crown including 8 pearls clear and distinct. A high degree of lustre or frost should remain.
REVERSE UNCIRCULATED, MS-60 — All detail in the wreath, crown and bow are sharp and maple boughs clearly defined.

OBVERSE ABOUT UNCIRCULATED, AU-50 — Very slight wear on shoulder bow, ear and crown. Half of mint lustre remaining.
REVERSE ABOUT UNCIRCULATED, AU-50 — Slight trace of wear on high points - knot in wreath, crown and lower leaves.

OBVERSE EXTREMELY FINE, EF-40 — Eyebrow worn. Slight wear on ear, moustache and side whiskers. Band of crown slightly worn but all jewels, including 8 pearls showing.
REVERSE EXTREMELY FINE, EF-40 — Trace of wear around the outer edges of lower leaves and centre arch of crown.

OBVERSE VERY FINE, VF-20 — Eyebrow, moustache and side whiskers considerably worn, also robe, shoulder bow and ornamental chain. Band of crown worn, but 4 to 6 pearls remain.
REVERSE VERY FINE, VF-20 — Wear on outer edges of leaves consists of about 1/3 their area. Central arch of crown shows slight wear.

OBVERSE FINE, F-12 — Robe, shoulder bow, jewels on chain and band of crown are worn considerably. At least half of band remains. Top of ear merges with hair.
REVERSE FINE, F-12 — Wear on leaves increased to about 1/2 their area. Pearls in the arches of crown begin to merge.

OBVERSE VERY GOOD, VG-8 — Band of crown is worn through in the centre. Only weak outline of robe, shoulder bow and chain remain. Outlines of ear is indistinct and moustache and beard are blurred.
REVERSE VERY GOOD, VG-8 — Very little detail remains in the leaves. Pearls in crown are blurred and the centre is often worn through.

OBVERSE GOOD, G-4 — Band of the crown and ear are worn away, also details of robe, chain, beard and moustache. Legend is weak.
REVERSE GOOD, G-4 — Leaves and crown badly worn with little but outlines remaining. Lettering and numerals are weak. Border beads blurred.

OBVERSE UNCIRCULATED, MS-60 — Robe, shoulder bow, crown and moustache all clearly defined. Ornamental chain detail sharp and clear. A high degree of lustre remains.
REVERSE UNCIRCULATED, MS-60 — No trace of wear showing on wreath, crown or bow. All detail on maple boughs sharp and clear.

OBVERSE ABOUT UNCIRCULATED, AU-50 — Very slight wear on moustache, crown, ear and hairlines. Half of mint lustre remaining.
REVERSE ABOUT UNCIRCULATED, AU-50 — Slight trace of wear on high points - knot in wreath, crown and lower leaves.

OBVERSE EXTREMELY FINE, EF-40 — Eyebrow worn. Band of crown slightly worn near centre but all 8 pearls showing. Trace of wear on tip of moustache and side whiskers. All 6 pearls down centre of crown are clearly defined.
REVERSE EXTREMELY FINE, EF-40 — Trace of wear around outer edges of most leaves and centre arch of crown.

OBVERSE VERY FINE, VF-20 — Eyebrow, moustache, beard and side whiskers are considerably worn, also robe, shoulder bow and ornamental chain. Band of crown is worn but 4 to 6 pearls remain, also at least 2 pearls at top of crown.
REVERSE VERY FINE, VF-20 — Wear on outer edges of leaves consists of about 1/3 their area. Slight wear on centre arch of crown.

OBVERSE FINE, F-12 — Jewels in the band of crown blurred, but 4 pearls and 1/2 to 3/4 of band remains. Eyebrow indistinct. Beard and moustache worn together. Details of robe, shoulder bow and chain begin to blur. Top of ear merges with hair.
REVERSE FINE, F-12 — Wear on leaves about 1/2 their area. Pearls in centre arch of crown begin to merge.

OBVERSE VERY GOOD, VG-8 — Band of crown is worn through in centre with only front and rear portions remaining. Eyebrow worn off. Little detail remains in robe, bow and chain.
REVERSE VERY GOOD, VG-8 — Very little detail remains in the leaves. Considerable wear on the centre arch of crown.

OBVERSE GOOD, G-4 — Band of crown worn away, also most of ear and other details. Legend is weak.
REVERSE GOOD, G-4 — Leaves and crown badly worn with little but outlines remaining. Lettering and numerals are weak.

OBVERSE UNCIRCULATED, MS-60 — Hairlines, ear, eyebrow all sharp and distinct. Could be a nick or some bag marks but a high degree of lustre still remains.
REVERSE UNCIRCULATED, MS-60 — No wear on lion or unicorn. All details in shield and crown sharp and clear.

OBVERSE ABOUT UNCIRCULATED, AU-50 — Only a slight trace of wear showing on cheek, ear and hairlines. Half of mint lustre remaining.
REVERSE ABOUT UNCIRCULATED, AU-50 — Very slight wear showing on shield. All details still sharp.

Many of the 50¢ pieces, particularily the 1947, 1947ML and 1948 were weakly struck in the area at the top left corner of shield and base of crown. The weakness should not be mistaken for wear on strictly uncirculated coins. This is, however, one of the first portions to wear on circulated coins.

OBVERSE EXTREMELY FINE, EF-40 — Slight wear at eyebrow, ear lobe and hair above ear. Sideburn in front of ear clearly showing.
REVERSE EXTREMELY FINE, EF-40 — Slight wear on thighs and forelegs of lion and unicorn. Trace of wear on details of crown and shield.

OBVERSE VERY FINE, VF-20 — Eyebrow indistinct. Hairlines above the ear and side of head are blurred. Exposed portions of ear and cheek-bone show wear. Sideburn barely showing.
REVERSE VERY FINE, VF-20 — Some overall wear on bodies of lion and unicorn. Slight wear at bottom of crown and top of shield.

OBVERSE FINE, F-12 — Eyebrow worn off. Only slight detail in hair between the ear and part in hair. Considerable wear on ear, facial features and back of neck.
REVERSE FINE, F-12 — Considerable wear on lion and unicorn, bottom of crown and upper portion of shield. Border beads begin to merge.

OBVERSE VERY GOOD, VG-8 — No detail in hair above ear. Outer rim of ear is worn flat and merges with hair. Much wear on nose and other facial features.
REVERSE VERY GOOD, VG-8 — Lion and unicorn worn. Crown and shield somewhat worn but most of details remain.

Young Head 1953 - 1964

OBVERSE UNCIRCULATED, MS-60 — All 11 leaves of laurel wreath, hairlines and shoulder strap sharply defined. High degree of lustre.
REVERSE UNCIRCULATED, MS-60 — No wear showing on lion or unicorn. All details in shield and crown sharp and clear.

OBVERSE ABOUT UNCIRCULATED, AU-50 — Very slight wear on hairlines, shoulder and laurel wreath. Half of mint lustre remaining.
REVERSE ABOUT UNCIRCULATED, AU-50 — Trace of wear on lion, unicorn and crown.

OBVERSE EXTREMELY FINE, EF-40 — Slight wear at eyebrow, cheek, shoulder and laurel wreath. All 11 leaves showing.
REVERSE EXTREMELY FINE, EF-40 — Slight wear on thighs and forelegs of lion and unicorn, and at base of crown and top of shield.

OBVERSE VERY FINE, VF-20 — Considerable wear at eyebrow, bottom of ear and hair between ear and forehead. Laurel wreath is worn but 8 to 10 leaves showing. Shoulder is worn but shoulder strap visible on that variety.
REVERSE VERY FINE, VF-20 — Slight wear on lion and unicorn and at base of crown and upper panels of shield.

ELIZABETH II

Young Head 1953 - 1964

OBVERSE FINE, F-12 — Much wear over entire portrait with few hairlines visible. Only faint outlines of the bottom of ear, nose and mouth remain. Outlines of 4 to 7 leaves showing.
REVERSE FINE, F-12 — Lion and unicorn considerably worn. Crown and shield slightly worn but most of details remain.

Mature Head 1965 -

OBVERSE UNCIRCULATED, MS-60 — No evidence of wear at eyebrow, the hair over the ear, temple and forehead. Drapery over the shoulder and band of the diadem sharply defined.
REVERSE UNCIRCULATED, MS-60 — No signs of wear on lion or unicorn. All details in shield and crown are sharp and clear.

OBVERSE ABOUT UNCIRCULATED, AU-50 — Slight trace of wear on cheek, hairlines, tiara and drapery on shoulder. Half of mint lustre remaining.
REVERSE ABOUT UNCIRCULATED, AU-50 — Very slight wear on lion, unicorn and crown.

OBVERSE EXTREMELY FINE, EF-40 — Slight wear at eyebrow and hair over the ear. Also hair at temple and forehead. Drapery over the shoulder will show slight wear, particularily the line at top of Queen's gown.
REVERSE EXTREMELY FINE, EF-40 — Slight wear on crown, front of helmet and the forelegs of the lion and unicorn.

PROVINCE OF CANADA
VICTORIA 1858-1859

The obverse design of the 1858-1859 cents was originally intended for an English coinage but was rejected owing to the inner beaded circle, which was similar to the bronze coinage of the Emperor Napoleon III of France.

The obverse shows a youthful Victoria with a laurel wreath in her hair. Reverse is a serpentine vine with 16 maple leaves. The 1¢, 5¢, 10¢ and 20¢ of 1858 and the cents of 1859 were issued by the Province of Canada but as they are mostly similar in appearance to the Dominion of Canada issues that followed, they are included in this listing.

G-4	- Braid worn through near ear.
VG-8	- No detail in braid around ear.
F-12	- Segments of braid begin to merge into one another.
VF-20	- Braid is clear but not sharp.
EF-40	- Braid is slightly worn but generally sharp and clear.
AU-50	- Slight traces of wear on high points. Degree of mint lustre still present.
MS-60	- No traces of wear. High degree of lustre.

Designer: Leonard C. Wyon.

Diameter: 25.400 mm; Weight: 4.536 grams; Composition: .950 copper, .040 tin, .010 zinc; Plain edge.

Date and Mint Mark	Quantity Minted	G-4	VG-8	F-12	VF-20	EF-40	AU-50	MS-60
1858	421,000	15.00	25.00	30.00	45.00	75.00	100.00	150.00

1859 Plain, Narrow 9

Double Punched Narrow 9
traces of original 9 at left.

In addition to the plain narrow 9 date on the 1859 cents, there are many varieties. The editor is listing those most widely collected.

A) 1859 double punched narrow 9, with traces of original 9 at left. Sometimes listed as re-engraved.

B) 1859 double punched narrow 9, resembling and usually identified as 9 over 8, narrow 9. Small piece out of die at lower left of 9, resulting in a deformity.

C) Wide 9 over 8. Some specimens of this variety have only a microscopic connection between the tail of the 9 and the upper loop, and have been classed as plain wide 9. Minor differences exist in the vine of maple leaves consisting of breaks in the stems.

Date and Mint Mark	Quantity Minted	G-4	VG-8	F-12	VF-20	EF-40	AU-50	MS-60
1859 Narrow 9	9,579,000*	.75	1.25	1.75	2.75	4.00	10.00	25.00
1859 Double Punched 9		18.00	30.00	40.00	50.00	80.00	125.00	175.00

Includes all 1859 cents.

Double Punched Narrow 9
resembles 9 over 8.

Wide 9, Over 8

Date and Mint Mark	Quantity Minted	G-4	VG-8	F-12	VF-20	EF-40	AU-50	MS-60
1859 Narrow 9 over 8		25.00	50.00	75.00	100.00	150.00	225.00	300.00
1859 Wide 9 over 8		13.00	20.00	25.00	35.00	50.00	75.00	100.00

DOMINION OF CANADA
VICTORIA 1876-1901

A change in the obverse design was made for the 1876 cent with a diademed Queen Victoria. The weight was increased from 4.536 to 5.670 grams. Pattern pieces exist with the 1858-1859 obverse and 1876 reverse.

G-4 - Hair over ear worn through.
VG-8 - No details in the hair over ear.
F-12 - Strands of hair over ear begin to run together.
VF-20 - Hair and jewels no longer sharp but clear.
EF-40 - Hair over ear is sharp and clear. Jewels in diadem must show sharply and clearly.
AU-50 - Slight traces of wear on high points. Degree of mint lustre still present.
MS-60 - No traces of wear. High degree of lustre.

Designer: Leonard C. Wyon.
Diameter: 25.400 mm; Weight: 5.670 grams; Composition: .950 copper, .040 tin, .010 zinc; Plain edge.

Date and Mint Mark	Quantity Minted	G-4	VG-8	F-12	VF-20	EF-40	AU-50	MS-60
1876H	4,000,000	.75	1.50	2.25	3.00	4.00	10.00	20.00
1881H	2,000,000	1.00	2.00	3.00	4.00	7.00	15.00	25.00
1882H	4,000,000	.75	1.35	2.25	3.25	4.50	8.50	15.00
1884	2,500,000	.85	1.75	2.50	3.50	5.50	10.00	20.00
1886	1,500,000	1.25	2.25	3.25	5.00	8.50	20.00	35.00
1887	1,500,000	1.25	2.25	3.25	5.00	8.50	20.00	35.00
1888	4,000,000	.80	1.40	1.85	2.75	3.75	9.00	18.00
1890H	1,000,000	2.50	5.00	7.00	10.00	13.50	25.00	40.00

1891 Large Date - Large Leaves
Leaves close to beaded circle and vine.

Date and Mint Mark	Quantity Minted	G-4	VG-8	F-12	VF-20	EF-40	AU-50	MS-60
1891 Lg. date-lg. leaves	1,452,500	2.50	5.00	7.00	9.00	13.50	25.00	40.00

1891 Small Date - Large Leaves
Leaves close to beaded circle and vine.

Date and Mint Mark	Quantity Minted	G-4	VG-8	F-12	VF-20	EF-40	AU-50	MS-60
1891 Sm. date-lg. leaves	Incl.	25.00	35.00	45.00	55.00	80.00	125.00	200.00

1891 Small Date - Small Leaves
Leaves farther from beaded circle and vine.

Date and Mint Mark	Quantity Minted	G-4	VG-8	F-12	VF-20	EF-40	AU-50	MS-60
1891 Sm. date-sm. leaves	Incl.	20.00	30.00	40.00	50.00	75.00	110.00	160.00
1892	1,200,000	1.50	2.75	3.75	5.50	8.75	15.00	25.00
1893	2,000,000	1.25	2.25	3.25	4.00	5.50	10.00	18.00
1894	1,000,000	3.50	6.00	8.00	10.00	15.00	30.00	50.00
1895	1,200,000	1.50	3.00	4.00	5.50	8.50	15.00	25.00
1896	2,000,000	.85	1.75	2.25	3.25	5.00	8.00	15.00
1897	1,500,000	.85	1.75	2.25	3.50	5.50	10.00	20.00

Note location of 'H' mint mark. On other large cents it appears under the date.

Date and Mint Mark	Quantity Minted	G-4	VG-8	F-12	VF-20	EF-40	AU-50	MS-60
1898H	1,000,000	2.00	3.50	5.00	8.00	12.00	17.50	30.00
1899	2,400,000	.65	1.25	2.00	2.50	4.00	8.00	15.00
1900	1,000,000	3.00	5.00	7.00	10.00	15.00	25.00	40.00
1900H	2,600,000	.85	1.75	2.25	3.25	4.75	8.00	14.00
1901	4,100,000	.65	1.25	1.50	2.50	3.50	7.00	12.00

EDWARD VII 1902 - 1910

The obverse depicts the crowned, robed bust of King Edward VII, with the chain of the Order of the Garter fastened by a bow on the shoulder. Designers initials DES below bust. The reverse is similar to the cents of Queen Victoria with serpentine vine of 16 maple leaves.

G-4 - Band of crown worn through.
VG-8 - Band of crown worn through at the highest point.
F-12 - Jewels in the band of crown will be blurred.
VF-20 - Band of the crown is still clear but no longer sharp.
EF-40 - Band of crown slightly worn but generally sharp and clear, including jewels.
AU-50 - Slight traces of wear on high points. Degree of mint lustre still present.
MS-60 - No traces of wear. High degree of lustre.

Designer: G.W. DeSaulles.

Diameter: 25.400 mm; Weight: 5.670 grams; Composition: .950 copper, .040 tin, .010 zinc; Plain edge.

Date and Mint Mark	Quantity Minted	G-4	VG-8	F-12	VF-20	EF-40	AU-50	MS-60
1902	3,000,000	.70	1.25	1.75	2.50	4.00	7.50	12.00
1903	4,000,000	.65	1.25	1.75	2.25	3.75	10.00	15.00
1904	2,500,000	1.00	1.75	2.75	3.50	5.00	10.00	15.00
1905	2,000,000	1.50	3.00	4.00	6.00	7.50	12.50	20.00
1906	4,100,000	.85	1.75	2.25	3.00	4.25	8.50	15.00
1907	2,400,000	1.00	2.00	3.00	4.00	6.00	10.00	15.00

Date and Mint Mark	Quantity Minted	G-4	VG-8	F-12	VF-20	EF-40	AU-50	MS-60
1907H	800,000	5.50	8.00	11.00	15.00	22.00	50.00	80.00
1908	2,401,506	1.00	2.00	2.50	3.50	5.00	10.00	15.00
1909	3,973,339	.80	1.25	1.50	2.50	4.00	6.00	10.00
1910	5,146,487	.75	1.25	1.50	2.50	3.50	6.00	10.00

GEORGE V 1911 - 1920

The obverse depicts King George V with chain of the Order of the Garter fastened by a bow on the shoulder. Designers initials BM at base of bust. The reverse is similar to the King Edward VII cents with continuous wreath of 16 maple leaves, but CANADA moved from obverse to reverse.

G-4	- Band of crown worn through.
VG-8	- Band of crown worn through at the highest point.
F-12	- Jewels in the band of crown will be blurred.
VF-20	- Band of crown is still clear but no longer sharp.
EF-40	- Band of crown slightly worn but generally sharp and clear, including jewels.
AU-50	- Slight traces of wear on high points. Degree of mint lustre still present.
MS-60	- No traces of wear. High degree of lustre.

Designers: Obverse - Sir E.B. MacKennal; Reverse - W.H.J. Blakemore.

Diameter: 25.400 mm; Weight: 5.670 grams; Composition: 1911-1919 - .950 copper, .040 tin, .010 zinc; 1919-1920 - .955 copper, .030 tin, .015 zinc; Plain edge.

Date and Mint Mark	Quantity Minted	G-4	VG-8	F-12	VF-20	EF-40	AU-50	MS-60
1911 Godless	4,663,486	.70	1.25	2.00	3.50	6.00	10.00	15.00
1912	5,107,642	.55	.90	1.25	1.75	2.75	5.00	8.00
1913	5,735,405	.55	.90	1.25	1.75	2.75	5.00	8.00
1914	3,405,958	.70	1.00	1.50	2.00	3.00	6.00	10.00
1915	4,932,134	.55	.90	1.25	1.75	2.75	5.00	7.00
1916	11,022,367	.55	.90	1.25	1.50	2.25	4.00	6.00
1917	11,899,254	.50	.75	1.00	1.50	2.25	4.00	6.00
1918	12,970,798	.50	.75	1.00	1.40	2.25	4.00	6.00
1919	11,279,634	.50	.75	1.00	1.40	2.25	4.00	6.00
1920	6,762,247	.50	.85	1.10	1.75	2.50	4.25	7.00

GEORGE V 1920 - 1936

For economy, a change was made from a large to small cent, about the same size and composition as the United States Lincoln cent. The obverse design was retained while a new reverse design, featuring two maple leaves, was used.

G-4	- Band of crown worn through.
VG-8	- Band of the crown is worn through at the highest point.
F-12	- Jewels in the band of crown will be blurred.
VF-20	- Band of the crown is still clear but no longer sharp.
EF-40	- Band of the crown slightly worn but generally sharp and clear, including jewels.
AU-50	- Slight traces of wear on high points. Degree of mint lustre still present.
MS-60	- No traces of wear. High degree of lustre.

Designers: Obverse - Sir E.B. MacKennal; Reverse - Fred Lewis.

Diameter: 19.050 mm; Weight: 3.240 grams; Composition: .955 copper, .030 tin, .015 zinc; Plain edge.

Date and Mint Mark	Quantity Minted	G-4	VG-8	F-12	VF-20	EF-40	AU-50	MS-60
1920	15,483,923	.15	.30	.50	1.25	2.00	4.00	7.00
1921	7,601,627	.25	.60	.90	2.25	3.75	7.50	12.00
1922	1,243,635	5.00	10.00	12.00	16.00	26.00	50.00	100.00
1923	1,019,002	12.00	18.00	24.00	30.00	40.00	80.00	150.00
1924	1,593,195	3.00	5.50	6.50	8.00	12.50	25.00	40.00
1925	1,000,622	8.00	13.00	16.00	20.00	30.00	60.00	100.00
1926	2,143,372	1.25	2.25	3.00	4.00	7.50	15.00	30.00
1927	3,553,928	.50	1.00	1.50	3.00	5.00	10.00	17.00
1928	9,144,860	.15	.25	.35	1.00	2.25	4.00	7.00
1929	12,159,840	.10	.25	.35	.90	2.25	4.00	6.50
1930	2,538,613	.75	1.50	2.00	3.50	7.00	13.50	20.00
1931	3,842,776	.50	1.00	1.50	2.25	4.00	8.00	16.00
1932	21,316,190	.10	.20	.25	.60	1.75	3.50	7.00
1933	12,079,310	.10	.20	.30	.55	1.75	3.50	6.00
1934	7,042,358	.15	.25	.40	1.00	2.00	4.00	7.00
1935	7,526,400	.15	.25	.40	1.00	2.00	4.00	7.00
1936	8,768,769	.10	.25	.35	.55	1.50	3.00	5.50

1936 with raised Dot - 678,823 minted

Four Specimens Known

1936 DOT COINAGE

The 'dot' coinage dated 1936 is actually an emergency issue of 1937, struck to cope with a shortage of 1¢, 10¢ and 25¢ pieces that came about while the new dies for King George VI were being prepared in London.

The Mint states categorically that all coins struck were immediately placed in circulation, but no satisfactory explanation of the great rarity of the two low values, as against the comparative commonness of the 25¢, has ever been suggested. Beware of counterfeit 'dot' 1¢ and 10¢ pieces. The author knows of no business strikes that were found in circulation and it is his opinion that none ever circulated.

GEORGE VI 1937 - 1952

The obverse portrait on George VI cent depicts a bare-headed King while the reverse design features a maple sprig with the designers initials K.G. under the right leaf.

VG-8	*- No details in hair above ear.*
F-12	*- Only slight detail in hair above the ear.*
VF-20	*- Where not worn, the hair is clear but not sharp.*
EF-40	*- Slight wear in hair over ear.*
AU-50	*- Slight traces of wear on high points. Degree of mint lustre still present.*
MS-60	*- No traces of wear. High degree of lustre.*

Designers: Obverse - T.H. Paget; Reverse - G.E. Kruger-Gray.

Diameter: 19.050 mm; Weight: 3.240 grams; Composition: 1937-1942 - .955 copper, .030 tin, .015 zinc; 1942-1952 - .980 copper, .005 tin, .015 zinc; Plain edge.

Date and Mint Mark	Quantity Minted	VG-8	F-12	VF-20	EF-40	AU-50	MS-60
1937	10,040,231	.20	.30	.75	1.25	1.75	2.00
1938	18,365,608	.15	.25	.45	.90	1.50	1.75
1939	21,600,319	.15	.25	.40	.90	1.25	1.60
1940	85,740,532	.10	.20	.30	.60	1.00	1.50
1941	56,336,011	.10	.20	.40	.70	2.00	3.25
1942	76,113,708	.10	.20	.40	.65	2.00	3.00
1943	89,111,969	.10	.20	.30	.50	1.00	1.25
1944	44,131,216	.10	.20	.40	.60	3.00	5.00
1945	77,268,591	.10	.15	.30	.55	.65	.75
1946	56,662,071	.10	.15	.30	.50	.65	.75
1947	31,093,901	.10	.15	.30	.50	.65	.75
1947 Maple Leaf	43,855,448	.10	.15	.25	.40	.85	1.25

Early in 1948 the new dies, with "Et Ind: Imp:" deleted as a result of India being given independence, were not ready and an emergency issue from the previous year's dies, with a tiny maple leaf as an identifying mark, had to be made of all 1948 issues until the new dies arrived late in the year.

Date and Mint Mark	Quantity Minted	VG-8	F-12	VF-20	EF-40	AU-50	MS-60
1948	25,767,779	.10	.20	.40	.50	1.50	2.25
1949	33,128,933	––	.10	.20	.25	.65	1.00
1950	60,444,992	––	.10	.20	.25	.50	.75
1951	80,430,379	––	.10	.15	.25	.45	.65
1952	67,631,736	––	.10	.15	.20	.45	.65

ELIZABETH II

LAUREATE BUST 1953 - 1964

The first issue of Queen Elizabeth depicts a laureate bust of the Queen with designers initials MG at base of bust. The reverse is similar to the King George VI cent.

F-12 - Leaves worn almost through, shoulder straps indistinct.

VF-20 - Leaves are considerably worn; straps must be clear.

EF-40 - Laurel leaves on the head are somewhat worn.

AU-50 - Traces of wear on hair. Degree of mint lustre still present.

MS-60 - No traces of wear. High degree of lustre.

Designers: Obverse - Mrs. Mary Gillick; Reverse - G.E. Kruger-Gray.

Diameter: 19.050 mm; Weight: 3.240 grams; Composition: .980 copper, .005 tin, .015 zinc; Plain edge.

No Shoulder Strap   Shoulder Strap

Note Different
Style Of Letters
And Position In
Relation To Beads

Apart from the first strikings of 1953 coins and a few 1954 and 1955 cents, the coins from 1953 to date have two prominent lines right over the Queen's shoulder, representing a fold in the gown, but resembling a strap, and they are known as the "shoulder strap" variety. Others with the lines almost missing at the top of the Queen's shoulder are termed "no shoulder strap".

Date and Mint Mark	Quantity Minted	F-12	VF-20	EF-40	AU-50	MS-60
1953 No Shoulder Strap	67,806,016	.10	.15	.25	.45	.60
1953 Shoulder Strap	Incl.	1.25	1.75	3.00	7.50	12.00
1954	22,181,760	.20	.25	.35	1.25	1.85
1954 No Shoulder Strap (PL)	Incl.	—	—	—	—	60.00
1955	56,403,193	—	.15	.25	.40	.50
1955 No Shoulder Strap	Incl.	—	25.00	35.00	42.50	50.00
1956	78,685,535	—	.15	.25	.40	.50
1957	100,601,792	—	.10	.15	.25	.35
1958	59,385,679	—	—	.10	.20	.25
1959	83,615,343	—	—	.10	.15	.20
1960	75,772,775	—	—	—	—	.15
1961	139,598,404	—	—	—	—	.15
1962	227,244,069	—	—	—	—	.15
1963	279,076,334	—	—	—	—	.15
1964	484,655,322	—	—	—	—	.15

MATURE HEAD 1965 -

A new portrait of the Queen was introduced in 1965. This is known as the Tiara or Mature Head. Minor varieties exist in the small cents of 1965.

MS-60 - *No traces of wear. High degree of lustre.*

Designer: Obverse - Arnold Machin; Reverse - G.E. Kruger-Gray.

Diameter: 19.050 mm; Weight: 3.240 grams; Composition: .980 copper, .005 tin, .015 zinc; Plain edge.

Large Beads   Small Beads

Pointed "5"   Blunt "5"

In the Large Beads (119) variety, the apex of letter "A" in Regina points to a bead. In Small Beads (121) variety, it points between two beads. Blunt 5 refers to the blunt right end of the horizontal bar of figure "5". Pointed 5 has a tapered right end.

Date and Mint Mark	Quantity Minted	MS-60
1965 Small Beads, Pointed 5, Variety 1	304,441,082	.30
1965 Small Beads, Blunt 5, Variety 2	Incl.	.05
1965 Large Beads, Blunt 5, Variety 3	Incl.	.15
1965 Large Beads, Pointed 5, Variety 4	Incl.	5.00
1966	183,644,388	.10

The Confederation Centennial reverse design by Alex Colville, was a rock dove. No change in the physical specifications.

Date and Mint Mark	Quantity Minted	MS-60
1967 Dove (Confederation)	345,140,645	.10
1968	329,695,772	.10
1969	335,240,929	.10
1970	311,145,010	.10
1971	298,228,936	.10
1972	451,304,591	.10
1973	457,059,852	.10
1974	692,058,489	.10
1975	642,318,000	.10
1976	701,122,890	.10
1977	453,762,670	.10
1978	914,375,639	.10
1979		.10

PROVINCE OF CANADA
VICTORIA 1858

The 5 cent silver coins often referred to as "fish scales" had a long and useful life, with few major changes, apart from monarchs, in 63 years. Minor variations in portrait are of no significance to most collectors.

G-4	- Braid worn through near ear.
VG-8	- No detail in braid around ear.
F-12	- Segments of braid begin to merge into one another.
VF-20	- Braid is clear but not sharp.
EF-40	- Braid is slightly worn but generally sharp and clear.
AU-50	- Slight traces of wear on high points. Degree of mint lustre still present.
MS-60	- No traces of wear. High degree of lustre.

Designer: Leonard C. Wyon.

Diameter: 15.500 mm; Weight: 1.162 grams; Composition: .925 silver, .075 copper; Reeded edge.

1858 Small Date
Note space between
figures in date.

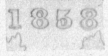

1858 Large Date
Figures in date are larger
and closer together.

Although the over punching is difficult to detect on some 1858 large date 5 cent pieces, it is now believed that all of these are the large date over small date variety.

Date and Mint Mark	Quantity Minted	G-4	VG-8	F-12	VF-20	EF-40	AU-50	MS-60
1858 Small Date	1,500,000	5.00	9.00	12.50	20.00	30.00	65.00	100.00
1858 Large Date	Incl.	65.00	100.00	135.00	190.00	275.00	425.00	650.00

DOMINION OF CANADA

VICTORIA 1870 - 1901

1870 Flat Border   **1870 Raised Border**

The 1870 5 cent piece is found with flat rim or border like that on the 1858 5 cents, and with high wire or raised border.

Date and Mint Mark		Quantity Minted	G-4	VG-8	F-12	VF-20	EF-40	AU-50	MS-60
1870	Flat Border	2,800,000	4.00	7.50	10.00	15.00	30.00	65.00	100.00
1870	Raised Border	Incl.	5.00	8.00	11.00	17.00	30.00	70.00	110.00
1871		1,400,000	4.50	7.00	10.00	15.00	25.00	60.00	100.00
1872H		2,000,000	3.25	5.50	8.00	13.00	23.00	75.00	125.00

1874 Plain 4

1874 Crosslet 4

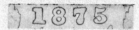

Large Date

Small Date

Date and Mint Mark	Quantity Minted	G-4	VG-8	F-12	VF-20	EF-40	AU-50	MS-60
1874H Plain 4	800,000	6.00	12.00	16.00	28.00	40.00	100.00	160.00
1874H Crosslet 4	Incl.	4.00	7.00	10.00	17.50	35.00	80.00	125.00
1875H Large Date	1,000,000	30.00	65.00	100.00	125.00	250.00	475.00	700.00
1875H Small Date	Incl.	25.00	50.00	75.00	100.00	200.00	350.00	450.00
1880H	3,000,000	1.50	2.75	4.00	7.00	16.00	50.00	85.00
1881H	1,500,000	2.50	3.75	5.00	10.00	18.00	50.00	85.00
1882H	1,000,000	3.00	4.50	6.50	11.00	22.00	60.00	95.00
1883H	600,000	4.50	8.00	16.00	22.00	38.00	80.00	125.00
1884	200,000	30.00	45.00	70.00	110.00	200.00	350.00	500.00
1885	1,000,000	3.25	5.50	7.50	11.00	25.00	60.00	95.00
1885 Over 83 (CNA 1976 SALE)	——	——	——	——	145.00	——	——	——

Large 6

Small 6

1900 Oval or Narrow 0's
With Small 9

1900 Round or Wide 0's
With Large 9

Date and Mint Mark	Quantity Minted	G-4	VG-8	F-12	VF-20	EF-40	AU-50	MS-60
1886 Large 6	1,700,000	1.75	3.00	4.25	7.50	15.00	50.00	100.00
1886 Small 6	Incl.	1.50	2.75	4.00	7.00	14.00	45.00	85.00
1887	500,000	4.50	8.50	12.00	18.00	30.00	75.00	150.00
1888	1,000,000	1.35	3.00	4.00	7.00	14.00	40.00	55.00
1889	1,200,000	7.50	15.00	20.00	30.00	60.00	125.00	175.00
1890H	1,000,000	2.00	3.25	5.00	9.00	18.00	50.00	85.00
1891	1,800,000	1.50	3.00	4.00	6.00	15.00	40.00	75.00
1892	860,000	2.50	4.50	7.00	12.00	18.00	45.00	80.00
1893	1,700,000	1.50	3.00	3.75	6.00	14.00	40.00	75.00
1894	500,000	5.00	9.00	14.00	20.00	30.00	70.00	120.00
1896	1,500,000	1.35	2.75	3.75	6.50	13.00	40.00	75.00
1897	1,319,283	1.35	2.75	3.75	6.50	13.00	40.00	70.00
1898	580,717	4.50	8.00	12.00	18.00	30.00	60.00	90.00
1899	3,000,000	1.00	2.00	3.00	4.50	10.00	35.00	65.00
1900 Oval 0	1,800,000	1.25	2.00	3.00	4.50	10.00	30.00	55.00
1900 Round 0	Incl.	6.00	12.00	18.00	25.00	40.00	80.00	125.00
1901	2,000,000	1.25	2.00	3.00	4.50	8.00	30.00	55.00

EDWARD VII 1902 - 1910

The Royal Crown as used on the Victorian silver was also used on all varieties of the 1902 5 cent silver because the Imperial Crown die was not ready. However, the Royal Crown was not a Queen's crown, as is commonly believed. The same type of crown was used on many British coins.

Obverse: shows a crowned Edward VII. Reverse: crossed maple boughs, tied at the bottom by a ribbon and separated at the top by a crown. The word CANADA moved to reverse of coin.

G-4 - *Band of crown worn through.*
VG-8 - *Band of crown worn through at the highest point.*
F-12 - *Jewels in the band of crown will be blurred.*
VF-20 - *Band of the crown is still clear but no longer sharp.*
EF-40 - *Band of crown slightly worn but generally sharp and clear, including jewels.*
AU-50 - *Slight traces of wear on high points. Degree of mint lustre still present.*
MS-60 - *No traces of wear. High degree of lustre.*

Designer: Obverse - G.W. DeSaulles.
Diameter: 15.50 mm; Weight: 1901-1907 - 1.162 grams, 1908-1910 - 1.166 grams; Composition: .925 silver, .075 copper; Reeded edge.

1902 no 'H'   1902 small 'H'   1902 large 'H'

Date and Mint Mark		Quantity Minted	G-4	VG-8	F-12	VF-20	EF-40	AU-50	MS-60
1902		2,120,000	.75	1.50	2.00	3.00	6.00	15.00	30.00
1902	Large Broad H	2,200,000	1.00	1.75	2.50	3.50	7.00	15.00	30.00
1902	Small Narrow H	Incl.	4.50	7.50	10.00	15.00	25.00	40.00	75.00
1903		1,000,000	1.00	2.50	4.50	8.00	15.00	50.00	90.00
1903H		2,640,000	1.00	2.00	3.00	4.00	7.00	20.00	40.00
1904		2,400,000	1.50	2.50	3.50	4.50	8.00	20.00	45.00
1905		2,600,000	1.50	2.50	3.50	4.50	8.00	20.00	40.00
1906		3,100,000	1.00	1.50	2.00	3.50	6.50	20.00	40.00
1907		5,200,000	.75	1.50	2.00	3.50	6.50	20.00	35.00
1908		1,220,524	3.00	4.50	7.00	10.00	15.00	30.00	55.00
1909		1,983,725	1.35	2.50	3.50	6.00	9.00	20.00	40.00
1910		5,850,325	.75	1.50	2.00	3.00	6.00	20.00	35.00

GEORGE V 1911 - 1936

Obverse: shows a crowned George V. Reverse: crossed maple boughs, tied at the bottom by a ribbon and separated at the top by a crown. The 1911 obverse had DEI GRATIA omitted. This was corrected on those of 1912-1921 with DEI GRA:.

G-4 - *Band of crown worn through.*
VG-8 - *Band of crown worn through at the highest point.*
F-12 - *Jewels in the band of crown will be blurred.*
VF-20 - *Band of crown is still clear but no longer sharp.*
EF-40 - *Band of crown slightly worn but generally sharp and clear, including jewels.*
AU-50 - *Slight traces of wear on high points. Degree of mint lustre still present.*
MS-60 - *No traces of wear. High degree of lustre.*

Designer: Obverse - G.W. DeSaulles.
Diameter: 15.50 mm; Weight: 1.166 grams; Composition: 1911-1919 - .925 silver, .075 copper, 1920-1921 - .800 silver, .200 copper; Reeded edge.

1921: 2,582,495 of the 5 cent silver pieces had been struck when it was decided to use a large nickel coin for this denomination. The silver pieces, including some of 1920, were then melted down. A few were obtained by those who ordered complete sets of coins from the mint and visitors to the mint in 1921. Approximately 200 known.

Date and Mint Mark	Quantity Minted	G-4	VG-8	F-12	VF-20	EF-40	AU-50	MS-60
1911	3,692,350	1.25	2.00	3.50	6.00	12.00	30.00	60.00
1912	5,863,170	.75	1.25	2.00	3.00	5.00	15.00	30.00
1913	5,588,048	.75	1.25	2.00	3.00	5.00	15.00	30.00
1914	4,202,179	.85	1.50	2.50	3.50	6.00	15.00	30.00
1915	1,172,258	3.00	4.50	7.50	12.00	24.00	65.00	95.00
1916	2,481,675	1.00	2.00	3.00	4.50	8.50	20.00	35.00
1917	5,521,373	.75	1.25	1.75	2.25	4.00	12.50	25.00
1918	6,052,298	.75	1.25	1.75	2.25	4.00	12.50	25.00
1919	7,835,400	.75	1.25	1.75	2.25	4.00	12.50	25.00
1920 Original	10,649,851	.75	1.25	1.75	2.25	4.00	12.50	25.00
1921 Original	2,582,495	700.00	1,000.00	1,250.00	1,750.00	2,500.00	4,500.00	6,500.00*

*New England Rare Coin Auction Sale of November 11, 1978.

GEORGE V 1922 - 1936

A change was made in 1922 to a nickel 5 cent coin as it was more convenient to use. Two varieties exist in the 1926 date.

G-4	- Band of crown worn through.
VG-8	- Band of the crown is worn through at the highest point.
F-12	- Jewels in the band of crown will be blurred.
VF-20	- Band of the crown is still clear but no longer sharp.
EF-40	- Band of the crown slightly worn but generally sharp and clear, including jewels.
AU-50	- Slight traces of wear on high points. Degree of mint lustre still present.
MS-60	- No traces of wear. High degree of lustre.

Designer: Sir E.B. MacKennal.
Diameter: 21.21 mm; Weight: 4.536 grams; Composition: 1.000 nickel; Plain edge.

1926 Near '6'   1926 Far '6'

In the near 6 variety the top of the figure 6 nearly touches the maple leaf. In the far 6 variety it is farther away. "Beware of altered 6".

Date and Mint Mark	Quantity Minted	G-4	VG-8	F-12	VF-20	EF-40	AU-50	MS-60
1922	4,794,119	.20	.35	.75	2.50	5.50	20.00	35.00
1923	2,502,279	.35	.55	1.25	3.75	9.00	35.00	60.00
1924	3,105,839	.25	.50	1.25	3.25	8.00	30.00	50.00
1925	201,921	16.00	25.00	32.50	65.00	150.00	300.00	450.00
1926 Near 6	938,162	2.00	3.00	4.50	15.00	50.00	100.00	150.00
1926 Far 6	Incl.	40.00	70.00	90.00	125.00	250.00	500.00	750.00

Date and Mint Mark	Quantity Minted	G-4	VG-8	F-12	VF-20	EF-40	AU-50	MS-60
1927	5,285,627	.25	.35	1.00	3.00	7.00	25.00	45.00
1928	4,577,712	.25	.35	1.00	3.00	7.00	25.00	45.00
1929	5,611,911	.25	.35	1.00	3.00	7.00	25.00	45.00
1930	3,704,673	.25	.35	1.00	3.00	7.00	25.00	45.00
1931	5,100,830	.25	.35	1.00	2.75	7.00	25.00	45.00
1932	3,198,566	.25	.40	1.00	2.75	7.00	27.50	50.00
1933	2,597,867	.35	.50	1.25	3.25	8.00	27.50	50.00
1934	3,827,304	.25	.35	1.00	3.00	7.50	25.00	45.00
1935	3,900,000	.20	.35	1.00	3.00	7.50	25.00	40.00
1936	4,400,450	.20	.35	1.00	3.00	7.00	25.00	40.00

GEORGE VI 1937 - 1952

The obverse portrait on George VI nickel depicts a bare-headed King with designers initials HP beneath bust. The new reverse shows a beaver on a rock and chewing at a log. Designers initials K.G. at left of log. Only the 1937 issue has the official round raised dot after date.

VG-8 - No details in hair above ear.
F-12 - Only slight detail in hair above the ear.
VF-20 - Where not worn, the hair is clear but not sharp.
EF-40 - Slight wear in hair over ear.
AU-50 - Slight traces of wear on high points. Degree of mint lustre still present.
MS-60 - No traces of wear. High degree of lustre.

Designer: Obverse - T.H. Paget; Reverse - G.E. Kruger-Gray.

Diameter: 1937-1942 - 21.210 mm; Weight: 4.536 grams; Composition: 1.000 nickel; Plain edge.

1942 Tombac   1943 Tombac

1942 - Owing to a scarcity of nickel as a result of war requirements, only a portion of the year's issue of 5 cent pieces was struck in this metal. A change was made to an alloy of 88% copper and 12% zinc, known as tombac, and the coin was made twelve-sided to distinguish it from the bronze cent.

1942-1943 "Tombac" (brass): Diameter: 21.23-21.29 mm (opposite corners), 20.88-20.93 (opposite sides); Weight: 4.536 grams; Composition: .880 copper, .120 zinc; Plain edge.

Date and Mint Mark	Quantity Minted	VG-8	F-12	VF-20	EF-40	AU-50	MS-60
1937 Dot After Date	4,593,263	.25	.75	2.50	4.00	12.00	20.00
1938	3,898,974	.35	1.25	3.50	12.00	43.50	75.00
1939	5,661,123	.25	.75	2.50	7.00	23.50	40.00
1940	13,920,197	.20	.50	1.50	4.00	14.50	25.00
1941	6,681,785	.20	.50	1.50	5.00	17.50	30.00
1942	6,847,544	.20	.50	1.50	5.00	16.00	27.00

1943 - A new design was used for the 1943 tombac 5 cent piece. It depicts on the reverse the letter V and a torch conjoined, emblematic of victory and sacrifice. The motto around the border, "We win when we work willingly", in International Code, was intended as an incentive to the war effort. This was the first die to be wholly prepared at the Royal Canadian Mint. The reverse of the 1943 Tombac 5 cent piece was designed by Thomas Shingles.

To December 1972 61% of all Tombacs have been withdrawn from circulation and melted.

1944 and 1945 - War demands on copper and zinc caused the discontinuance of the tombac 5 cent pieces. The coin was struck in steel with the 1943 design, coated with a .0127 mm layer of nickel and plated with a .0003 mm layer of chromium.

Collectors should beware of steel coins that have been plated to look like uncirculated pieces.

Date and Mint Mark	Quantity Minted	VG-8	F-12	VF-20	EF-40	AU-50	MS-60
1942 Tombac Beaver	3,396,234	.75	1.00	1.25	1.50	2.75	4.00
1943 Tombac V	24,760,256	.35	.50	.75	1.00	2.50	4.00
1944 Steel V	11,532,784	.20	.30	.50	.75	1.75	2.50
1945 Steel V	18,893,216	.20	.30	.50	.75	1.75	2.50

1946-1950: Nickel was used again for coinage of the 5 cent piece. The design reverted to that of the pre-war 5 cent piece, but the coin remained twelve-sided.

Date and Mint Mark	Quantity Minted	VG-8	F-12	VF-20	EF-40	AU-50	MS-60
1946 Nickel Beaver	6,952,684	.20	.35	.75	3.00	6.00	9.00
1947 Nickel Beaver	7,603,724	.20	.35	.75	2.00	5.00	8.00

1947 Dot Beaver   1947 Maple Leaf Beaver

A variety of the 1947 nickel has a tiny round raised dot at the lower right of figure 7. This resulted from a pit in the chromium plating on one of the dies. There is a similar variety of the 1947 twenty-five cent piece and dollar and many others too numerous to list in a standard catalogue.

Date and Mint Mark	Quantity Minted	VG-8	F-12	VF-20	EF-40	AU-50	MS-60
1947 Dot Beaver		8.00	12.50	25.00	50.00	325.00	600.00
1947 Maple Leaf Beaver	9,595,124	.20	.30	.75	2.00	5.00	8.00

Early in 1948, the new dies with "Et Ind: Imp:" deleted as a result of India being given independence, were not ready and an emergency issue from the previous year's dies, with a tiny maple leaf as an identifying mark, had to be made of all 1948 issues until the new dies arrived late in the year.

Date and Mint Mark	Quantity Minted	VG-8	F-12	VF-20	EF-40	AU-50	MS-60
1948 Nickel Beaver	1,810,789	.75	1.00	2.00	5.00	12.50	20.00
1949 Nickel Beaver	13,037,090	.20	.25	.50	1.00	3.00	5.00
1950 Nickel Beaver	11,970,520	.20	.25	.50	1.00	3.00	5.00

1951 Nickel

1951 Steel

1951 - The 5 cent piece commemorates the two hundredth anniversary of the isolation of the metal nickel by a Swedish chemist in 1751. A conventionalized refinery is the central motif. Late in the year, a shortage of nickel led to a change to the normal beaver design in chromium-plated steel, and this was continued until 1955 when nickel was again used for the coinage.

1951 Nickel Commemorative	9,028,507	.20	.25	.45	.60	1.50	2.50

1951 - 1952 Beaver
   same composition as 1944 - 1945 Steel V and same size.

Low Relief Portrait

High Relief Portrait

Date and Mint Mark	Quantity Minted	VG-8	F-12	VF-20	EF-40	AU-50	MS-60
1951 Steel Beaver							
High Relief Obverse		——	25.00	50.00	100.00	150.00	200.00
Low Relief Obverse	4,313,410	.25	.35	.70	1.25	4.50	7.50
1952 Steel Beaver	10,891,148	.20	.25	.50	.75	2.25	4.00

ELIZABETH II

LAUREATE BUST 1953 - 1964

First strikings of 1953 with a high relief portrait proved unsatisfactory. The relief was then lowered and hair and shoulder re-engraved. These later coins have two prominent lines over Queen's shoulder, representing a fold in the gown but resembling a shoulder strap. They are known as shoulder strap variety. There are also differences in the style of lettering and position of legend relative to rim denticles. In 1962 for the first time, the 5 cent coin was struck from nickel blanks fabricated in Canada.

F-12 - Leaves worn almost through, shoulder straps indistinct.
VF-20 - Leaves are considerably worn; straps must be clear.
EF-40 - Laurel leaves on the head are somewhat worn.
AU-50 - Traces of wear on hair. Degree of mint lustre still present.
MS-60 - No traces of wear. High degree of lustre.

Designer: Obverse - Mrs. Mary Gillick; Reverse - G.E. Kruger-Gray.

Diameter: 1953-1962 - 21.23-21.29 mm (opposite corners), 20.88-20.93 mm (opposite sides), 1963-1964 - 21.21 mm; Weight: 4.536 grams; Composition: 1953-1954 - steel, coated with .0127 mm layer of nickel and plated with a .0003 layer of chomium, 1955-1964 - 1.000 nickel; Plain edge.

No Shoulder Strap   Shoulder Strap

Date and Mint Mark	Quantity Minted	VG-8	F-12	VF-20	EF-40	AU-50	MS-60
1953 Steel Beaver - NSS	16,635,552	.20	.25	.50	1.00	2.50	4.00
1953 Steel Beaver - SS	Incl.	.20	.25	.60	1.50	3.75	6.00
1954 Steel Beaver	6,998,662	.25	.50	1.00	1.75	5.00	8.00
1955 Nickel Beaver	5,355,028	——	.25	.50	1.00	3.00	5.00
1956 Nickel Beaver	9,399,854	——	——	.25	.50	1.25	2.00
1957 Nickel Beaver	7,387,703	——	——	.25	.50	1.25	2.00
1958 Nickel Beaver	7,607,521	——	——	.25	.50	1.25	2.00
1959 Nickel Beaver	11,552,523	——	——	.15	.25	.65	1.00
1960 Nickel Beaver	37,157,433	——	——	——	.20	.35	.50
1961 Nickel Beaver	47,889,051	——	——	——	——	——	.30
1962 Nickel Beaver	46,306,306	——	——	——	——	——	.30

1964 Extra Water Line

Date and Mint Mark	Quantity Minted	F-12	VF-20	EF-40	AU-50	MS-60
1963 Nickel Beaver - Round	43,970,320	——	——	——	——	.25
1964 Nickel Beaver	78,075,068	——	——	——	——	.25
1964 Extra Water Line	Incl.	5.00	6.00	10.00	15.00	20.00

MATURE HEAD 1965 -

MS-60   - No traces of wear. High degree of lustre.

A new mature draped bust portrait by Arnold Machin of the Queen wearing a diamond tiara was introduced. No change was made in the reverse or physical specifications.

Date and Mint Mark	Quantity Minted	EF-40	AU-50	MS-60
1965	84,876,019	——	——	.25
1966	27,678,469	——	——	.25

The Confederation Centennial reverse design by Alex Colville was a rabbit. No change was made in the physical specifications.

Date and Mint Mark	Quantity Minted	EF-40	AU-50	MS-60
1967 Rabbit (Confederation)	36,876,574	--	--	.25
1968	99,253,330	--	--	.20
1969	27,830,229	--	--	.20
1970	5,726,010	.25	.45	.60
1971	27,312,609	--	--	.20
1972	62,417,387	--	--	.15
1973	53,507,435	--	--	.15
1974	94,704,645	--	--	.15
1975	138,882,000	--	--	.15
1976	55,140,213	--	--	.15
1977	89,120,791	--	--	.15
1978	137,077,187	--	--	.15
1979		--	--	.15

PROVINCE OF CANADA
VICTORIA 1858

A ten cent denomination was included in the first decimal coinage struck for the Province of Canada in 1858. The obverse depicts a laureate head of the Queen with the hair tied in a knot at the back. The reverse has St. Edward's crown at the top, crossed maple boughs, tied at the bottom by a ribbon.

G-4 - Braid worn through near ear.
VG-8 - No detail in braid around ear.
F-12 - Segments of braid begin to merge into one another.
VF-20 - Braid is clear but not sharp.
EF-40 - Braid is slightly worn but generally sharp and clear.
AU-50 - Slight traces of wear on high points. Degree of mint lustre still present.
MS-60 - No traces of wear. High degree of lustre.

Designer: Leonard C. Wyon.

Diameter: 1858 - 18.000 mm, 1870-1901 - 18.034 mm; Weight: 1858-1901 - 2.324 grams; Composition: .925 silver, .075 copper; Plain edge.

Date and Mint Mark	Quantity Minted	G-4	VG-8	F-12	VF-20	EF-40	AU-50	MS-60
1858	1,250,000	5.00	10.00	15.00	35.00	70.00	150.00	225.00

DOMINION OF CANADA
VICTORIA 1870 - 1901

The 1858 design was continued on the Dominion of Canada 1870-1901 ten cent coinage. Some insignificant variations exist in the Queen's portrait during this period.

Date and Mint Mark		Quantity Minted	G-4	VG-8	F-12	VF-20	EF-40	AU-50	MS-60
1870	Narrow 0	1,600,000	3.75	7.50	15.00	25.00	60.00	150.00	225.00
1870	Wide 0	Incl.	4.50	9.00	15.00	30.00	65.00	150.00	225.00
1871		800,000	5.00	10.00	16.00	35.00	70.00	180.00	300.00
1871H		1,870,000	8.50	17.00	25.00	35.00	75.00	175.00	275.00
1872H		1,000,000	25.00	50.00	75.00	125.00	200.00	350.00	500.00
1874H		600,000	3.50	6.00	12.00	25.00	50.00	140.00	225.00
1875H		1,000,000	55.00	100.00	150.00	275.00	500.00	850.00	1,250.00
1880H		1,500,000	3.00	5.00	10.00	20.00	45.00	140.00	225.00
1881H		950,000	4.00	7.50	16.00	26.00	50.00	125.00	200.00
1882H		1,000,000	3.00	5.00	10.00	20.00	45.00	125.00	200.00
1883H		300,000	9.00	17.50	35.00	65.00	135.00	250.00	400.00
1884		150,000	42.50	80.00	150.00	300.00	600.00	850.00	1,250.00
1885		400,000	5.00	10.00	20.00	50.00	110.00	200.00	300.00

1886 Small 6   1886 Large 6

1886	Small 6	800,000	5.00	10.00	20.00	45.00	85.00	165.00	250.00
1886	Large 6	Incl.	5.00	10.00	20.00	45.00	85.00	165.00	250.00
1887		350,000	7.50	15.00	25.00	70.00	150.00	350.00	600.00
1888		500,000	3.50	5.00	8.00	20.00	45.00	125.00	200.00
1889		600,000	175.00	300.00	500.00	1,000.00	1,500.00	2,500.00	3,500.00
1890H		450,000	4.50	9.00	18.00	40.00	85.00	200.00	300.00

1891 10¢ - 21 Leaves (small leaf missing)   22 Leaves

1893 Flat Top 3   1893 Round Top 3
(The 3 is usually weak)

1899 Large 9's in Date   1899 Small 9's in Date

Date and Mint Mark	Quantity Minted	G-4	VG-8	F-12	VF-20	EF-40	AU-50	MS-60
1891 21 Leaves	800,000	4.50	9.00	17.00	35.00	60.00	150.00	225.00
1891 22 Leaves	Incl.	4.50	9.00	18.00	35.00	65.00	160.00	250.00
1892	520,000	3.50	7.00	15.00	30.00	55.00	110.00	175.00
1893 Flat Top 3	500,000	5.00	10.00	20.00	40.00	70.00	140.00	210.00
1893 Round Top 3	Incl.	200.00	350.00	700.00	1,000.00	2,500.00	5,000.00	9,000.00
1894	500,000	3.00	6.00	12.00	20.00	45.00	120.00	200.00
1896	650,000	2.75	5.00	11.00	20.00	45.00	100.00	175.00
1898	720,000	2.50	5.00	11.00	20.00	45.00	120.00	200.00
1899 Small 9's	1,200,000	2.00	4.00	7.00	18.00	40.00	100.00	175.00
1899 Large 9's	Incl.	4.00	7.00	13.00	35.00	70.00	150.00	225.00
1900	1,100,000	1.50	3.00	6.00	18.00	35.00	75.00	135.00
1901	1,200,000	1.50	3.00	6.00	18.00	35.00	75.00	135.00

EDWARD VII 1902 - 1910

The obverse depicts King with crown and robe, wearing the collar of the Order of the Garter, fastened by a bow on the shoulder. The word CANADA is moved from obverse to reverse. The wreath with Victorian type leaves (22) was continued until 1909 when large broad leaves were substituted. The Imperial Crown was used on the reverse.

G-4 - *Band of crown worn through.*
VG-8 - *Band of crown worn through at the highest point.*
F-12 - *Jewels in the band of crown will be blurred.*
VF-20 - *Band of the crown is still clear but no longer sharp.*
EF-40 - *Band of crown slightly worn but generally sharp and clear, including jewels.*
AU-50 - *Slight traces of wear on high points. Degree of mint lustre still present.*
MS-60 - *No traces of wear. High degree of lustre.*

Designer: Obverse - G.W. DeSaulles.

Diameter: 18.034 mm; Weight: 1902-1907 - 2.324 grams, 1908-1910 - 2.333 grams; Composition: .925 silver, .075 copper; Reeded edge.

Date and Mint Mark	Quantity Minted	G-4	VG-8	F-12	VF-20	EF-40	AU-50	MS-60
1902	720,000	2.00	4.00	7.00	12.00	35.00	110.00	200.00
1902H	1,100,000	1.50	3.00	6.00	10.00	25.00	60.00	100.00
1903	500,000	3.00	6.00	12.00	30.00	65.00	125.00	200.00
1903H	1,320,000	1.50	3.00	5.00	12.00	30.00	75.00	135.00
1904	1,000,000	3.25	6.50	12.00	30.00	60.00	120.00	200.00
1905	1,000,000	2.50	5.00	10.00	25.00	55.00	115.00	200.00
1906	1,700,000	2.00	4.00	7.00	18.00	40.00	100.00	175.00
1907	2,620,000	1.50	3.00	6.00	12.00	25.00	75.00	135.00
1908	776,666	1.75	3.50	6.00	16.00	35.00	90.00	150.00

1909 Large Leaves (same as Victorian)	1909 Broad Leaves
Top Right Leaves Resembling Three Individual Leaves Similar To Those From 1902 to 1908	Top Right Leaves Resembling One Large Leaf Similar To Those From 1910 to 1912

Date and Mint Mark	Quantity Minted	G-4	VG-8	F-12	VF-20	EF-40	AU-50	MS-60
1909 Large Leaves	1,697,200	2.00	4.00	7.00	15.00	35.00	110.00	200.00
1909 Broad Leaves	Incl.	2.25	4.50	9.00	25.00	45.00	115.00	200.00
1910	4,468,331	1.25	2.50	4.50	9.00	25.00	75.00	125.00

GEORGE V 1911 - 1936

The obverse depicts King with crown and robe, wearing the collar of the Order of the Garter, fastened by a bow on the shoulder. The reverse has Imperial Crown, crossed maple boughs and broad leaves from 1911 to 1913. A change was then made to small leaves but a scarce variety of the 1913 exists with the broad leaves. D.G. was omitted from the 1911 obverse and DEI GRA: was inserted on the 1912. Designers initials B.M. appear below bust.

G-4 - Band of crown worn through.
VG-8 - Band of crown worn through at the highest point.
F-12 - Jewels in the band of crown will be blurred.
VF-20 - Band of crown is still clear but no longer sharp.
EF-40 - Band of crown slightly worn but generally sharp and clear, including jewels.
AU-50 - Slight traces of wear on high points. Degree of mint lustre still present.
MS-60 - No traces of wear. High degree of lustre.

Designer: Obverse - Sir E.B. MacKennel.

Diameter: 18.034 mm; Weight: 2.333 grams; Composition: 1911-1919 - .925 silver, .075 copper, 1920-1936 - .800 silver, .200 copper; Reeded edge.

1913 Small Leaves   Broad Leaves   1936 with Raised Dot

1936 Dot coins were struck in 1937. Not a single authenticated specimen of the 1936 Dot 10¢ piece has been found in circulation and the author believes none ever circulated. Beware of counterfeits.

Date and Mint Mark	Quantity Minted	G-4	VG-8	F-12	VF-20	EF-40	AU-50	MS-60
1911 No D.G.	2,737,584	6.00	12.00	16.00	30.00	70.00	150.00	250.00
1912	3,235,557	.75	1.50	2.50	5.00	14.00	50.00	85.00
1913 Small Leaves	3,613,937	.75	1.25	2.25	4.50	12.00	50.00	85.00
1913 Broad Leaves	Incl.	35.00	65.00	110.00	225.00	450.00	850.00	1,300.00
1914	2,549,811	.75	1.50	3.00	6.50	14.00	40.00	75.00
1915	688,057	2.50	5.00	10.00	35.00	100.00	250.00	450.00
1916	4,218,114	.70	1.00	1.50	4.00	10.00	30.00	60.00
1917	5,011,988	.70	1.00	1.75	3.50	9.00	25.00	55.00
1918	5,133,602	.70	1.00	1.75	3.50	8.00	25.00	55.00
1919	7,877,722	.70	1.00	1.75	3.50	8.00	25.00	55.00
1920	6,305,345	.70	1.00	1.75	4.00	8.00	25.00	55.00
1921	2,469,562	.75	1.25	2.00	4.75	10.00	30.00	60.00
1928	2,458,602	.75	1.25	2.00	4.50	9.00	25.00	50.00
1929	3,253,888	.75	1.25	1.75	4.50	8.00	25.00	50.00
1930	1,831,043	.75	1.25	1.75	4.50	8.00	25.00	55.00
1931	2,067,421	.75	1.25	2.00	4.50	8.00	27.50	60.00
1932	1,154,317	.75	1.25	2.50	6.00	10.00	40.00	80.00
1933	672,368	1.00	2.00	4.00	8.00	25.00	50.00	90.00
1934	409,067	1.25	2.50	4.50	9.00	25.00	75.00	150.00
1935	384,056	1.50	2.50	5.00	15.00	35.00	125.00	250.00
1936	2,460,871	.55	1.00	1.50	3.50	8.00	25.00	50.00
*1936 Raised Dot	191,237	ONLY 4 KNOWN: SPECIMEN - VERY RARE						

GEORGE VI 1937 - 1952

The obverse depicts the bare-headed King and the text "ET IND: IMP:" on the 1937-1947 issue. From 1948-1952 "ET IND: IMP:" was omitted becuase India was granted independence from England in 1947.

As one of the series of new designs for the 1937 coinage, the famous fishing and racing schooner "Bluenose" appears on the 10 cent coin. A member of the Emmanuel Hahn family informed the author that the designer used the Bluenose as the model for design. His initial H appears above the water at left. The small date on 1937 issue wore off so a larger date and higher in field was used from 1938.

VG-8 - No details in hair above ear.
F-12 - Only slight detail in hair above the ear.
VF-20 - Where not worn, the hair is clear but not sharp.
EF-40 - Slight wear in hair over ear.
AU-50 - Slight traces of wear on high points. Degree of mint lustre still present.
MS-60 - No traces of wear. High degree of lustre.

Designer: Emmanuel Hahn.

Diameter: 18.034 mm; Weight: 2.333 grams; Composition: .800 silver, .200 copper; Reeded edge.

Date and Mint Mark	Quantity Minted	VG-8	F-12	VF-20	EF-40	AU-50	MS-60
1937	2,500,095	2.25	3.50	5.50	8.50	14.25	20.00
1938	4,197,323	.90	2.50	5.00	10.00	37.50	65.00
1939	5,501,748	.75	1.50	4.00	8.00	24.00	40.00
1940	16,526,470	.60	1.00	2.50	4.00	9.50	15.00
1941	8,716,386	.75	1.50	3.00	8.00	29.00	50.00
1942	10,214,011	.60	1.00	2.00	4.00	22.00	40.00
1943	21,143,229	.60	1.00	2.00	3.25	10.75	18.00
1944	9,383,582	.60	1.00	2.25	3.00	14.00	25.00
1945	10,979,570	.60	.85	1.50	2.50	8.75	15.00
1946	6,300,066	.60	.90	1.75	3.00	16.50	30.00
1947	4,431,926	.75	1.25	3.25	7.75	28.75	50.00
1947 Maple Leaf	9,638,793	.60	.85	1.50	2.00	8.50	15.00

1948	422,741	5.00	6.50	12.00	25.00	47.50	70.00
1949	11,336,172	.40	.60	.80	1.35	4.75	8.00
1950	17,823,075	.40	.60	.80	1.35	4.25	7.00
1951	15,079,265	.40	.60	.80	1.35	4.25	7.00
1952	10,474,455	.40	.60	.80	1.35	4.00	6.50

ELIZABETH II

LAUREATE BUST 1953 - 1964

High relief laureate portrait of Queen on dies used early in 1953 resulted in poorly struck coins, so relief was lowered to 3/4 and hair and shoulder details re-engraved. See text on cent for more detail.

Early strikings are distinguished by lack of so-called "shoulder strap" on Queen's shoulder, detail of lettering and positioning of denticles in relation to letters. Designer initials M.G. at base of bust. No change in reverse design.

F-12	Leaves worn almost through, shoulder straps indistinct.
VF-20	Leaves are considerably worn; straps must be clear.
EF-40	Laurel leaves on the head are somewhat worn.
AU-50	Traces of wear on hair. Degree of mint lustre still present.
MS-60	No traces of wear. High degree of lustre.

Designers: Obverse - Mrs. Mary Gillick, Reverse - Emmanuel Hahn.

Diameter: 18.034 mm; Weight: 2.333 grams; Composition: .800 silver, .200 copper; Reeded edge.

No Shoulder Strap   Shoulder Strap

Date and Mint Mark	Quantity Minted	VG-8	F-12	VF-20	EF-40	AU-50	MS-60
1953 No Shoulder Strap	17,706,395	.40	.50	.75	1.25	3.00	4.50
1953 Shoulder Strap	Incl.	.40	.60	1.00	2.00	5.25	8.50
1954	4,493,150	.75	1.00	1.50	2.50	6.25	10.00
1955	12,237,294	.40	.50	.75	1.25	3.00	4.50
1956	16,732,844	.40	.50	.75	1.00	2.25	3.50

1956 10-Cent With Dot

Due to a defective die, a variety of the 1956 10-cent piece occurs with a tiny raised dot below the centre of the date. This is one of many mint errors which are listed in variety catalogues.

Date and Mint Mark	Quantity Minted	VG-8	F-12	VF-20	EF-40	AU-50	MS-60
1956 Dot	Incl.	2.50	3.50	4.50	6.00	10.50	15.00
1957	16,110,229	——	.50	.75	1.00	1.25	1.50
1958	10,621,236	——	.50	.75	1.00	1.50	2.00
1959	19,691,433	——	——	.50	.75	1.00	1.25
1960	45,446,835	——	——	——	.50	.75	1.00
1961	26,850,859	——	——	——	.50	.75	1.00
1962	41,864,335	——	——	——	.50	.75	1.00
1963	41,916,208	——	——	——	.50	.65	.75
1964	49,518,549	——	——	——	.50	.65	.75

ELIZABETH II 1965

A new mature draped bust portrait of the Queen wearing a diamond tiara was introduced. No change was made in the reverse or physical specifications.

MS-60 - *No traces of wear. High degree of lustre.*

Designers: Obverse - Arnold Machin; Reverse - E. Hahn.
Diameter: 18.034 mm; Weight: 2.333 grams (silver), 2.0735 grams (nickel); Composition: 1968 - .500 silver, .500 copper, 1968 - 1.000 nickel; Reeded edge.

Date and Mint Mark	Quantity Minted	MS-60
1965	56,965,392	.65
1966	34,330,199	.65

The Confederation Centennial reverse design by Alex Colville was a mackerel. A change from .800 fine silver to .500 fine silver was made during the year.

Date and Mint Mark	Quantity Minted	MS-60
1967 Mackerel (.800 Fine Silver)	32,309,135	.50
1967 Mackerel (.500 Fine Silver)	30,689,080	.50
1968 (.500 Fine Silver)	70,460,000	.50

Philadelphia Mint
Flat
Cavity Edge

Ottawa Mint
V-Shaped
Cavity Edge

The schooner reverse was resumed in 1968 and a change from .500 fine silver to nickel was made on August 1st. About half of the latter were struck at the Philadelphia Mint, and are distinguished by the flat bottom grooves of the reeded edge. The nickel issue is a darker colour and attracted to a magnet.

Date and Mint Mark	Quantity Minted	MS-60
1968 Nickel, Phil. Mint, Flat Cavity Edge	85,170,000	.40
1968 Nickel, Ottawa Mint, V-Shaped Cavity Edge	87,412,930	.40

1969 Large Date   1969 Small Date

A small quantity of the 1969 issue consisted of a large schooner and large date, similar to the 1968. This variety is rare. Regular issue has a small schooner and small date.

Date and Mint Mark	Quantity Minted	MS-60
1969 Large Date, Large Ship - RARE	Incl. below	——
1969 Re-designed Reverse - Small Date, Small Ship	55,833,929	.30
1970	5,249,296	.60
1971	41,016,968	.30
1972	60,169,387	.30
1973	167,715,435	.30
1974	201,566,565	.30
1975	207,680,000	.30
1976	95,018,533	.30
1977	128,452,206	.30
1978	170,394,846	.25
1979		.20

PROVINCE OF CANADA
20 CENTS - VICTORIA 1858

The obverse depicts a youthful Victoria with a laurel wreath in her hair. Reverse - crossed maple boughs, tied at the bottom by a ribbon and separated at the top by St. Edward's crown. This single year issue was unpopular due to confusion with the 25 cent pieces of the United States and Dominion of Canada. The majority were withdrawn from circulation and melted.

G-4   - *Braid worn through near ear.*
VG-8   - *No detail in braid around ear.*
F-12   - *Segments of braid begin to merge into one another.*
VF-20 - *Braid is clear but not sharp.*
EF-40 - *Braid is slightly worn but generally sharp and clear.*
AU-50 - *Slight traces of wear on high points. Degree of mint lustre still present.*
MS-60 - *No traces of wear. High degree of lustre.*

Designer: L.C. Wyon.

Diameter: 23.266 mm; Weight: 4.648 grams; Composition: .925 silver, .075 copper; Reeded edge.

Date and Mint Mark	Quantity Minted	G-4	VG-8	F-12	VF-20	EF-40	AU-50	MS-60
1858	*750,000	30.00	45.00	55.00	85.00	150.00	450.00	800.00

*The majority were recalled and melted after 1870.

DOMINION OF CANADA
25 CENTS - VICTORIA 1870 - 1901

Obverse - crowned bust of Victoria facing left. Reverse - crossed maple boughs, tied at the bottom by a ribbon and separated at the top by St. Edward's crown. Some insignificant variations exist in the facial features of portrait and reverse wreath as a result of re-engraving origina designs.

G-4   - *Hair over ear worn through.*
VG-8   - *No details in the hair over ear.*
F-12   - *Strands of hair over ear begin to run together.*
VF-20 - *Hair and jewels no longer sharp but clear.*
EF-40 - *Hair over ear is sharp and clear. Jewels in diadem must show sharply and clearly.*
AU-50 - *Slight traces of wear on high points. Degree of mint lustre still present.*
MS-60 - *No traces of wear. High degree of lustre.*

Designer: L.C. Wyon.

Diameter: 23.662 mm; Weight: 5.810 grams; Composition: .925 silver, .075 copper; Reeded edge.

Date and Mint Mark	Quantity Minted	G-4	VG-8	F-12	VF-20	EF-40	AU-50	MS-60
1870	900,000	5.00	9.00	15.00	35.00	70.00	225.00	400.00
1871	400,000	6.00	12.00	20.00	40.00	80.00	225.00	400.00
1871H	748,000	6.00	12.00	18.00	40.00	80.00	225.00	400.00
1872H	2,240,000	3.00	5.00	10.00	20.00	40.00	175.00	300.00
1874H	1,600,000	5.00	5.00	10.00	20.00	40.00	175.00	300.00
1875H	1,000,000	85.00	125.00	250.00	600.00	1,200.00	2,000.00	3,500.00

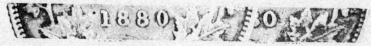

1880H Narrow 0	Wide 0

Date and Mint Mark	Quantity Minted	G-4	VG-8	F-12	VF-20	EF-40	AU-50	MS-60
1880H Narrow 0	400,000	8.00	15.00	25.00	60.00	125.00	350.00	600.00
1880H Wide 0	Incl.	27.50	45.00	90.00	180.00	375.00	600.00	850.00
1881H	820,000	5.50	9.00	16.00	50.00	100.00	225.00	400.00
1882H	600,000	6.00	11.00	20.00	50.00	110.00	225.00	400.00
1883H	960,000	4.00	7.00	12.00	32.00	65.00	200.00	375.00
1885	192,000	30.00	50.00	85.00	160.00	300.00	700.00	1,200.00
1886	540,000	5.00	9.00	17.00	45.00	90.00	275.00	500.00
1887	100,000	27.50	40.00	65.00	125.00	250.00	500.00	800.00
1888	400,000	5.00	8.00	18.00	45.00	95.00	200.00	325.00
1889	66,324	30.00	50.00	80.00	150.00	400.00	1,000.00	1,500.00
1890H	200,000	7.50	12.00	20.00	45.00	95.00	275.00	500.00
1891	120,000	12.00	20.00	40.00	80.00	160.00	375.00	600.00
1892	510,000	4.50	8.00	16.00	35.00	75.00	175.00	300.00
1893	100,000	15.00	25.00	50.00	100.00	200.00	375.00	600.00
1894	220,000	5.00	9.00	19.00	40.00	85.00	235.00	425.00
1899	415,580	3.00	5.00	8.00	20.00	45.00	125.00	225.00
1900	1,320,000	2.50	5.00	7.00	17.00	35.00	125.00	225.00
1901	640,000	3.00	5.00	8.00	20.00	40.00	125.00	225.00

EDWARD VII 1902 - 1910

Obverse - crowned, robed bust of the King with the chain of the Order of the Garter, fastened by a bow on the shoulder. Reverse - crossed maple boughs, tied at bottom by a ribbon and separated at the top by the Imperial State Crown. "CANADA" moved from obverse to reverse. Designers initials DES below bust.

G-4	- Band of crown worn through.
VG-8	- Band of crown worn through at the highest point.
F-12	- Jewels in the band of crown will be blurred.
VF-20	- Band of the crown is still clear but no longer sharp.
EF-40	- Band of crown slightly worn but generally sharp and clear, including jewels.
AU-50	- Slight traces of wear on high points. Degree of mint lustre still present.
MS-60	- No traces of wear. High degree of lustre.

Designer: G.W. DeSaulles.

Diameter: 23.622 mm; Weight: 5.810 grams, 1908-1910 - 5.832 grams; Composition: .925 silver, .075 copper; Reeded edge.

Date and Mint Mark	Quantity Minted	G-4	VG-8	F-12	VF-20	EF-40	AU-50	MS-60
1902	464,000	3.00	6.00	10.00	21.00	45.00	100.00	200.00
1902H	800,000	2.25	4.00	7.50	20.00	40.00	90.00	175.00
1903	846,150	3.00	6.00	12.00	35.00	70.00	175.00	300.00
1904	400,000	5.00	10.00	25.00	60.00	125.00	350.00	600.00
1905	800,000	3.00	6.00	12.00	35.00	75.00	200.00	350.00
1906	1,237,843	3.00	6.00	12.00	25.00	65.00	150.00	250.00
1907	2,088,000	3.00	6.00	12.00	25.00	65.00	150.00	250.00
1908	495,016	3.00	6.00	12.00	30.00	75.00	140.00	235.00
1909	1,335,929	3.00	5.00	8.00	18.00	75.00	175.00	300.00
1910	3,577,569	2.00	4.00	6.00	15.00	45.00	100.00	160.00

GEORGE V 1911 - 1936

Obverse - crowned, robed bust of the King with the chain of the Order of the Garter, fastened by a bow on the shoulder. Reverse - crossed maple boughs, tied at the bottom by a ribbon and separated at the top by the Imperial State Crown. Designers initials at base of bust. DEI GRATIA omitted on 1911 issue and DEI GRA: used from 1912.

G-4 - Band of crown worn through.
VG-8 - Band of crown worn through at the highest point.
F-12 - Jewels in the band of crown will be blurred.
VF-20 - Band of crown is still clear but no longer sharp.
EF-40 - Band of crown slightly worn but generally sharp and clear, including jewels.
AU-50 - Slight traces of wear on high points. Degree of mint lustre still present.
MS-60 - No traces of wear. High degree of lustre.

Designer: Obverse - Sir E.B. MacKennal.

Diameter: 23.622 mm; Weight: 5.832 grams; Composition: 1911-1919 - .925 silver, .075 copper, 1920-1936 - .800 silver, .200 copper; Reeded edge.

Date and Mint Mark	Quantity Minted	G-4	VG-8	F-12	VF-20	EF-40	AU-50	MS-60
1911 "Godless"	1,721,341	8.00	15.00	30.00	65.00	150.00	275.00	400.00
1912	2,544,199	1.50	2.50	4.00	12.00	35.00	80.00	150.00
1913	2,213,595	1.50	2.50	4.00	12.00	35.00	80.00	150.00
1914	1,215,397	2.00	3.50	5.00	15.00	40.00	100.00	200.00
1915	242,382	5.00	10.00	20.00	75.00	225.00	500.00	1,000.00
1916	1,462,566	2.00	3.00	5.00	12.00	30.00	75.00	135.00
1917	3,365,644	1.00	2.00	3.00	10.00	25.00	60.00	100.00
1918	4,175,649	1.00	2.00	3.00	10.00	25.00	60.00	100.00
1919 Originally	5,852,262	1.00	2.00	3.00	10.00	25.00	60.00	100.00
1920	1,975,278	1.25	2.50	4.00	10.00	30.00	70.00	120.00
1921	597,337	5.00	8.00	20.00	50.00	125.00	450.00	800.00
1927	468,096	8.00	15.00	30.00	75.00	150.00	400.00	600.00
1928	2,114,178	1.00	2.00	3.00	10.00	22.00	75.00	150.00
1929	2,690,562	1.00	2.00	3.50	10.00	22.00	75.00	150.00
1930	968,748	1.25	2.50	4.00	12.00	30.00	100.00	200.00
1931	537,815	1.75	3.00	6.50	15.00	45.00	135.00	250.00
1932	537,994	2.00	3.50	7.00	18.00	45.00	135.00	250.00
1933	421,282	2.00	3.50	7.00	18.00	45.00	130.00	225.00
1934	384,350	2.00	3.50	7.00	18.00	50.00	125.00	225.00
1935	537,772	1.50	3.00	6.00	15.00	40.00	100.00	200.00
1936	972,094	1.00	2.00	4.00	12.00	30.00	60.00	100.00

A small raised dot on some 1936 25¢ coins, indicates that they were struck in 1937. This issue has a convex reverse and "CAN" of "CANADA" is particularly subject to wear and is usually weaker than the rest of the legend. There are only 4 known in Specimen condition.

Date and Mint Mark	Quantity Minted	G-4	VG-8	F-12	VF-20	EF-40	AU-50	MS-60
1936 Dot	153,322	12.50	25.00	50.00	100.00	200.00	500.00	900.00

GEORGE VI 1937 - 1952

Obverse - bare-headed bust of George VI facing left. Reverse - caribou. Designers initials H.P. below bust. H under caribou's neck.

VG-8 — No details in hair above ear.
F-12 — Only slight detail in hair above the ear.
VF-20 — Where not worn, the hair is clear but not sharp.
EF-40 — Slight wear in hair over ear.
AU-50 — Slight traces of wear on high points. Degree of mint lustre still present.
MS-60 — No traces of wear. High degree of lustre.

Designers: Obverse - T.H. Paget, Reverse - Emmanuel Hahn.

Diameter: 23.622 mm; Weight: 5.832 grams; Composition: .800 silver, .200 copper; Reeded edge.

Date and Mint Mark	Quantity Minted	VG-8	F-12	VF-20	EF-40	AU-50	MS-60
1937	2,690,176	2.00	3.00	5.00	10.00	20.00	30.00
1938	3,149,245	2.00	3.00	6.00	10.00	47.50	85.00
1939	3,532,495	2.00	3.00	6.00	10.00	47.50	85.00
1940	9,583,650	1.25	2.50	3.50	7.50	13.75	20.00
1941	6,654,672	1.25	2.50	3.50	7.50	13.75	20.00
1942	6,935,871	1.25	2.50	3.50	7.50	16.25	25.00
1943	13,559,575	1.25	2.00	2.50	5.00	15.00	25.00
1944	7,216,237	1.25	2.00	2.50	5.00	27.50	50.00
1945	5,296,495	1.25	2.00	2.50	5.00	15.00	25.00
1946	2,210,810	1.50	2.50	5.00	12.00	41.00	70.00
1947	1,524,554	1.50	2.50	5.00	12.00	56.00	100.00

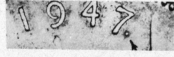 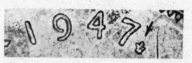

1947 Dot - a tiny irregular dot after the date resulted from a pitted or otherwise defective die.
1947 Maple Leaf - a small maple leaf after the date indicates the coin was struck in 1948.

Date and Mint Mark	Quantity Minted	VG-8	F-12	VF-20	EF-40	AU-50	MS-60
1947 Dot	Incl.	20.00	30.00	50.00	75.00	262.50	450.00
1947 Maple Leaf	4,393,938	1.25	1.75	2.50	3.50	9.25	15.00

1948 - ET IND: IMP: omitted from obv. as India granted independence from England in 1947.

1948	2,564,424	2.00	3.00	5.00	8.50	26.75	45.00
1949	7,988,830	1.25	1.75	2.25	3.50	7.75	12.00
1950	9,673,335	1.25	1.50	2.00	3.00	7.50	12.00
1951	8,290,719	— —	1.25	1.75	2.50	6.25	10.00
1952	8,859,642	— —	1.25	1.75	2.50	6.25	10.00

ELIZABETH II
LAUREATE BUST 1953 - 1964

Obverse - young head laureate bust of Queen Elizabeth facing right. Reverse - caribou. Designers initials M.G. at base of bust and H under caribou's neck.

F-12	- Leaves worn almost through, shoulder straps indistinct.
VF-20	- Leaves are considerably worn; straps must be clear.
EF-40	- Laurel leaves on the head are somewhat worn.
AU-50	- Traces of wear on hair. Degree of mint lustre still present.
MS-60	- No traces of wear. High degree of lustre.

Designer: Obverse - Mrs. Mary Gillick, Reverse - Emmanuel Hahn.

Diameter: 23.622 mm, 1953 small date to 1964 - 23.876 mm; Weight: 5.832 grams; Composition: .800 silver, .200 copper; Reeded edge.

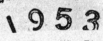

Large Date - Wire Rim	Small Date - Flat Rim

1953 - Major varieties exist in early large date, wire rim, no shoulder strap and later small date, flat rim, shoulder strap.

Date and Mint Mark	Quantity Minted	VG-8	F-12	VF-20	EF-40	AU-50	MS-60
1953 Lg. Date, Wire Rim, NSS	10,456,769	1.25	1.50	2.00	2.75	6.50	10.00
1953 Sm. Date, Flat Rim, SS	Incl.	——	1.35	2.00	2.75	6.50	10.00
1954	2,318,891	2.00	3.00	6.00	14.00	34.50	55.00
1955	9,552,505	——	1.25	1.75	2.75	6.00	9.00
1956	11,269,353	——	1.25	1.50	2.00	3.75	5.50
1957	12,770,190	——	1.25	1.50	2.00	3.00	3.75
1958	9,336,910	——	1.25	1.50	2.00	3.00	3.75
1959	13,503,461	——	——	1.25	1.50	2.25	2.75
1960	22,835,327	——	——	——	1.25	1.50	1.75
1961	18,164,368	——	——	——	——	——	1.50
1962	29,559,266	——	——	——	——	——	1.50
1963	21,180,652	——	——	——	——	——	1.25
1964	36,479,343	——	——	——	——	——	1.25

MATURE HEAD 1965 -

A new portrait by Arnold Machin depicts a mature draped bust of the Queen wearing a diamond tiara. No change was made in the reverse or the physical specifications.

MS-60	- No traces of wear. High degree of lustre.

Designers: Obverse - Arnold Machin; Reverse - Emmanual Hahn.

1968 .500 silver - Diameter: 23.876 mm; Weight: 5.832 grams (silver), 5.054 grams (nickel). 1968 to date 1.000 nickel - other specifications the same.

Date and Mint Mark	Quantity Minted	EF-40	AU-50	MS-60
1965 New Obverse Portrait	44,708,869	––	––	1.25
1966	25,626,315	––	––	1.25

The Confederation Centennial reverse design by Alex Colville was a wildcat (bobcat). A change from .800 fine silver to .500 fine silver was made during the year.

The caribou reverse was resumed in 1968 and a change from .500 fine silver to pure nickel was made on August 1st. The nickel coin is darker and is attracted to a magnet.

Date and Mint Mark	Quantity Minted	EF-40	AU-50	MS-60
1967 Wildcat (Confederation)	49,136,303	––	––	1.25
1968 .500 Fine Silver	71,464,000	––	––	1.25
1968 Nickel	88,686,931	––	––	1.25
1969	133,037,929	––	––	.65
1970	10,302,010	1.00	2.00	3.00
1971	48,170,428	––	––	.55
1972	43,743,387	––	––	.55

Type I
1973 - 25¢
Large Bust
132 Obv. Beads

Type II
1973 - 25¢
Small Bust
120 Obv. Beads

The special reverse on the 25 cent coin of 1973 commemorates the centennial of the founding of the Royal Canadian Mounted Police. Obverse dies of 1972 were used on a small quantity of the early strikings of the 1973 issue and these have the large bust. A newly engraved smaller portrait with more hair details was used for the large regular production. It also has a smaller number of obverse beads, which are farther from the rim.

Type I Variety found in a few proof-like sets and a small quantity in circulation.

Although no mintage figures are available, it is possible to estimate from information received, less than 1,000 in proof-like sets and less than 10,000 released for circulation.

In 1974 the large bust obverse was again used and the caribou reverse resumed.

Date and Mint Mark	Quantity Minted	EF-40	AU-50	MS-60
1973 R.C.M.P., Small Bust	134,958,589	––	––	.55
1973 R.C.M.P., Large Bust	Incl.	50.00	60.00	150.00
1974	192,360,598	––	––	.55
1975	141,148,000	––	––	.55
1976	86,898,261	––	––	.55
1977	99,634,555	––	––	.55
1978 Large Beads, 120 Denticles	175,953,251	––	––	.50
1978 Small Beads, 148 Denticles	Incl.	––	––	5.00
1979				.50

DOMINION OF CANADA
VICTORIA 1870 - 1901

Obverse - crowned bust of Victoria facing left. Reverse - crossed maple boughs, tied at the bottom by a ribbon and separated at the top by St. Edward's crown. Some insignificant variations exist in the facial features of portrait and reverse wreath as a result of re-engraved original design. Varieties exist in 1870 and 1872 issues.

G-4 - Hair over ear worn through.
VG-8 - No details in the hair over ear.
F-12 - Strands of hair over ear begin to run together.
VF-20 - Hair and jewels no longer sharp but clear.
EF-40 - Hair over ear is sharp and clear. Jewels in diadem must show sharply and clearly.
AU-50 - Slight traces of wear on high points. Degree of mint lustre still present.
MS-60 - No traces of wear. High degree of lustre.

Designer: L.C. Wyon.

Diameter: 29.72 mm; Weight: 11.620 grams; Composition: .925 silver, .075 copper; Reeded edge.

Beware of the 1870 with LCW and shamrock removed. On the LCW variety there is a shamrock behind the front cross in crown.
This is missing on the variety without LCW.

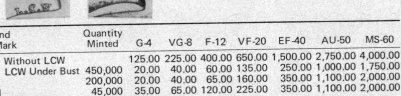

Date and Mint Mark		Quantity Minted	G-4	VG-8	F-12	VF-20	EF-40	AU-50	MS-60
1870	Without LCW		125.00	225.00	400.00	650.00	1,500.00	2,750.00	4,000.00
1870	LCW Under Bust	450,000	20.00	40.00	60.00	135.00	250.00	1,000.00	1,750.00
1871		200,000	20.00	40.00	65.00	160.00	350.00	1,100.00	2,000.00
1871H		45,000	35.00	65.00	120.00	225.00	350.00	1,100.00	2,000.00

A variety of the 1872H has an Inverted A Over V in the word "VICTORIA" on the obverse legend.

Date and Mint Mark	Quantity Minted	G-4	VG-8	F-12	VF-20	EF-40	AU-50	MS-60
1872H	80,000	17.50	35.00	60.00	135.00	250.00	1,000.00	2,000.00
1872H Inverted A Over V	Incl.	25.00	45.00	90.00	175.00	325.00	1,500.00	2,500.00

Date and Mint Mark	Quantity Minted	G-4	VG-8	F-12	VF-20	EF-40	AU-50	MS-60
1881H	150,000	17.50	35.00	65.00	135.00	250.00	1,000.00	1,700.00
1888	60,000	40.00	80.00	160.00	325.00	550.00	1,500.00	2,700.00
1890H	20,000	300.00	375.00	600.00	1,000.00	2,000.00	5,000.00	9,000.00
1892	151,000	17.50	35.00	65.00	135.00	250.00	1,100.00	2,000.00
1894	29,036	60.00	110.00	225.00	450.00	1,000.00	2,500.00	4,500.00
1898	100,000	15.00	30.00	60.00	115.00	250.00	1,100.00	2,000.00
1899	50,000	35.00	55.00	110.00	225.00	450.00	1,500.00	3,000.00
1900	118,000	15.00	30.00	55.00	110.00	250.00	1,000.00	1,800.00
1901	80,000	18.00	35.00	60.00	125.00	275.00	1,000.00	1,800.00

EDWARD VII 1902 - 1910

Obverse - crowned, robed bust of Edward VII facing right with the chain of the Order of the Garter, fastened by a bow on the shoulder. Reverse - crossed maple boughs, tied at the bottom by a ribbon, and separated at the top by the Imperial State Crown. Designers initials DES below bust. "CANADA" moved from obverse to reverse.

G-4 — *Band of crown worn through.*
VG-8 — *Band of crown worn through at the highest point.*
F-12 — *Jewels in the band of crown will be blurred.*
VF-20 — *Band of the crown is still clear but no longer sharp.*
EF-40 — *Band of crown slightly worn but generally sharp and clear, including jewels.*
AU-50 — *Slight traces of wear on high points. Degree of mint lustre still present.*
MS-60 — *No traces of wear. High degree of lustre.*

Designer: G.W. DeSaulles.
Diameter: 29.72 mm; Weight: 1902-1907 - 11.620 grams, 1908-1910 - 11.664 grams; Composition: .925 silver, .075 copper; Reeded edge.

Date and Mint Mark	Quantity Minted	G-4	VG-8	F-12	VF-20	EF-40	AU-50	MS-60
1902	120,000	8.00	16.00	45.00	125.00	300.00	600.00	1,200.00
1903H	140,000	15.00	25.00	50.00	150.00	350.00	700.00	1,500.00
1904	60,000	35.00	70.00	135.00	275.00	625.00	1,300.00	3,000.00
1905	40,000	35.00	70.00	135.00	300.00	700.00	1,750.00	3,500.00
1906	350,000	7.00	12.00	33.00	85.00	200.00	500.00	1,000.00
1907	300,000	7.00	12.00	33.00	85.00	200.00	500.00	1,000.00
1908	128,119	10.00	18.00	50.00	110.00	200.00	400.00	600.00
1909	203,118	7.00	13.00	40.00	85.00	200.00	500.00	1,000.00
1910	649,521	7.00	10.00	27.00	80.00	175.00	450.00	900.00

GEORGE V 1911 - 1936

Obverse - crowned, robed bust of the King with the chain of the Order of the Garter, fastened by a bow on the shoulder. Reverse - crossed maple boughs, tied at the bottom by a ribbon and separated at the top by the Imperial State Crown. Designers initials at base of bust. DEI GRATIA omitted on 1911 issue and DEI GRA: used from 1912.

50 Cents

G-4	- Band of crown worn through.
VG-8	- Band of crown worn through at the highest point.
F-12	- Jewels in the band of crown will be blurred.
VF-20	- Band of crown is still clear but no longer sharp.
EF-40	- Band of crown slightly worn but generally sharp and clear, including jewels.
AU-50	- Slight traces of wear on high points. Degree of mint lustre still present.
MS-60	- No traces of wear. High degree of lustre.

Designer: Sir E.B. MacKennal.
Diameter: 29.72 mm; Weight: 11.664 grams; Composition: 1911-1919 - .925 silver, .075 copper, 1920-1936 - .800 silver, .200 copper; Reeded edge.

Date and Mint Mark	Quantity Minted	G-4	VG-8	F-12	VF-20	EF-40	AU-50	MS-60
1911	209,972	10.00	15.00	80.00	350.00	950.00	1,200.00	1,500.00
1912	285,867	4.00	6.00	15.00	60.00	175.00	600.00	1,200.00
1913	265,889	4.00	7.00	15.00	60.00	175.00	600.00	1,200.00
1914	160,128	12.00	25.00	55.00	150.00	350.00	1,000.00	2,000.00
1916	459,070	4.00	9.00	15.00	40.00	125.00	400.00	800.00
1917	752,213	3.00	5.00	15.00	30.00	125.00	250.00	400.00
1918	854,989	3.00	5.00	15.00	35.00	125.00	250.00	400.00
1919	1,113,429	3.00	5.00	15.00	35.00	115.00	225.00	350.00
1920 Original	584,691	3.50	7.00	16.00	45.00	125.00	350.00	600.00

Due to lack of demand from 1920 to 1928, the reserves of 480,392 50 cent pieces dated 1920 and 1921 were melted and re-coined in 1929. It was felt that brand new outdated coins would arouse suspicions as to their genuineness. All of the remaining 1921 issue was included in the melt and only about 75 exist today. A few of these wer issued in specimen sets.

Date and Mint Mark	Quantity Minted	G-4	VG-8	F-12	VF-20	EF-40	AU-50	MS-60
1921	206,398	4,000.00	6,000.00	9,000.00	12,000.00	18,000.00	24,000.00	35,000.00*
1929	228,328	3.00	5.00	15.00	35.00	95.00	250.00	500.00
1931	57,581	6.00	10.00	20.00	60.00	150.00	600.00	1,200.00
1932	19,213	30.00	50.00	80.00	225.00	450.00	1,000.00	2,000.00
1934	39,539	8.00	15.00	30.00	75.00	225.00	550.00	1,000.00
1936	38,550	8.00	15.00	30.00	60.00	200.00	375.00	600.00

*New England Rare Coin Auction Sale of November 11, 1978.

GEORGE VI 1937 - 1952

Obverse - bare-headed bust of George VI facing left. Reverse - Canadian Coat of Arms. Designers initials, obv. - H.P. below bust, rev. - K.G. flanking crown.

VG-8	No details in hair above ear.
F-12	Only slight detail in hair above the ear.
VF-20	Where not worn, the hair is clear but not sharp.
EF-40	Slight wear in hair over ear.
AU-50	Slight traces of wear on high points. Degree of mint lustre still present.
MS-60	No traces of wear. High degree of lustre.

Designer: Obverse - T.H. Paget, Reverse - G.E. Kruger-Gray.

Diameter: 29.72 mm; Weight: 11.664 grams; Composition: .800 silver, .200 copper; Reeded edge.

Many of the 50 cent pieces from 1937 to 1948 were weakly struck on the reverse at the upper left corner of shield, not to be mistaken for wear.

New reverse introduced in 1937 shows between supporters the Canadian Coat of Arms in a shield surmounted by the Imperial Crown. The quarter panels are representative of England (a lion), Ireland (a harp), Scotland (rampant lion), France (three fleur-de-lis). A stem of three maple leaves is in the bottom panel. A rampant lion at left holds a lance flying the Union Jack and the unicorn on the right holds a lance flying the flag of Royalist France.

Date and Mint Mark	Quantity Minted	VG-8	F-12	VF-20	EF-40	AU-50	MS-60
1937	192,016	4.00	6.00	12.00	20.00	50.00	90.00
1938	192,018	4.50	6.50	15.00	75.00	150.00	275.00
1939	287,976	3.00	5.00	12.50	25.00	75.00	150.00
1940	1,996,566	2.75	3.50	5.00	7.00	15.00	30.00
1941	1,714,874	2.75	3.50	5.00	8.00	15.00	30.00
1942	1,974,165	2.75	3.50	5.00	8.00	15.00	30.00
1943	3,109,583	2.75	3.50	5.00	8.00	15.00	30.00
1944	2,460,205	2.75	3.50	5.00	8.00	15.00	30.00
1945	1,959,528	2.75	3.50	5.00	8.00	15.00	30.00
1946	950,235	3.25	4.50	7.00	14.00	60.00	125.00

1946 Design in
Centre of 6

1946 - Design in centre of 6, and 1949 Hoof. Defective dies caused these mint error coins.

Date and Mint Mark	Quantity Minted	VG-8	F-12	VF-20	EF-40	AU-50	MS-60
1946 Design in Centre of 6	Incl.	17.00	25.00	40.00	100.00	400.00	700.00

Straight 7
Points to Left

Curved 7
Points to Right

1947 - Two different figure 7's were used. The straight 7 is longer and points to the left. The curved 7 is shorter and points to the right.

Date and Mint Mark	Quantity Minted	VG-8	F-12	VF-20	EF-40	AU-50	MS-60
1947 Straight 7, Points Left	424,885	4.50	6.00	10.00	20.00	70.00	125.00
1947 Curved 7, Points Right	Incl.	4.50	6.00	10.00	20.00	70.00	125.00

Maple Leaf
Straight 7 Points Left

Maple Leaf
Curved 7 Points Right

1947 Maple Leaf - The small maple leaf after the date indicates the coins were struck in 1948. One variety has the straight 7 and maple leaf and the other, which is rare, has the curved 7 and a maple leaf. No official mintage figures are available but a total of 1,086 business strikes reported by a mint official, plus a small number for specimen sets.

Date and Mint Mark	Quantity Minted	VG-8	F-12	VF-20	EF-40	AU-50	MS-60
1947 ML, Straight 7, Points Left	38,433	35.00	45.00	65.00	90.00	150.00	225.00
1947 ML, Curved 7, Points Right	Incl.	1,000.00	1,300.00	1,600.00	2,000.00	2,400.00	3,000.00

1949 Hoof over 9

1948 ET IND: deleted from obverse as India granted independence from England in 1947. Specifications same as 1937-1947 issues.

Date and Mint Mark	Quantity Minted	VG-8	F-12	VF-20	EF-40	AU-50	MS-60
1948	37,784	50.00	65.00	90.00	125.00	175.00	250.00
1949	858,991	3.25	4.25	6.00	10.00	30.00	70.00
1949 Hoof Over 9	Incl.	10.00	15.00	30.00	55.00	250.00	600.00

1950
No Design in 0

1950
Design in 0

1950 - No design in 0. In polishing the die, the lines were inadvertently removed.

There are many other mint error 50 cent pieces of George VI resulting from cracked or broken dies similar to those listed but too numerous or unimportant to list in a standard catalogue.

Date and Mint Mark	Quantity Minted	VG-8	F-12	VF-20	EF-40	AU-50	MS-60
1950 No Design	2,384,179	8.00	10.00	15.00	35.00	125.00	300.00
1950 Design	Incl.	2.50	3.50	4.50	6.00	7.00	17.00
1951	2,421,730	2.50	3.00	4.25	5.50	6.50	13.50
1952	2,596,465	2.50	3.00	4.25	5.50	6.50	13.50

ELIZABETH II

LAUREATE BUST 1953 - 1964

Obverse - young head laureate bust of Queen Elizabeth. Reverse - Canadian Coat of Arms. Designers initials, obv. - M.G. at bottom of bust; rev. - E.H. flanking the crown.

F-12 - *Leaves worn almost through, shoulder straps indistinct.*
VF-20 - *Leaves are considerably worn; straps must be clear.*
EF-40 - *Laurel leaves on the head are somewhat worn.*
AU-50 - *Traces of wear on hair. Degree of mint lustre still present.*
MS-60 - *No traces of wear. High degree of lustre.*

Designers: Obverse - Mrs. Mary Gillick; Reverse - Emmanuel Hahn.
Diameter: 29.72 mm; Weight: 11.664 grams; Composition: .800 silver, .200 copper; Reeded edge.

Small Date

Large Date

1953 Major Varieties - early strikings: small date, no shoulder strap; later productions: large date, shoulder strap. A rare variety exists with large date and no shoulder strap. In 1955 the reverse was re-designed and the shield reduced in size.

Date and Mint Mark	Quantity Minted	VG-8	F-12	VF-20	EF-40	AU-50	MS-60
1953 Small Date, NSS	1,630,429	2.50	3.00	4.00	6.00	10.00	15.00
1953 Large Date, SS	Incl.	3.00	4.00	5.00	12.00	30.00	60.00
1953 Large Date, NSS		10.00	20.00	30.00	60.00	175.00	300.00
1954	506,305	3.00	4.00	8.00	15.00	30.00	60.00
1955	753,511	3.00	4.00	5.00	7.00	20.00	35.00
1956	1,379,499	––	2.50	3.00	4.00	5.00	10.00
1957	2,171,689	––	––	2.50	3.00	3.50	6.00
1958	2,957,266	––	––	2.50	3.00	3.50	6.00

A new Canadian Coat of Arms modeled and engraved by Thomas Shingles was introduced on the reverse of the 1959 50 cent coin. The shield is spade-shaped with a lion holding a maple leaf at the top. The shield is flanked by a lion holding a Union Jack on the left and a unicorn holding a fleur-de-lis on the right.
Strays of heroldic flowers are below the ribbon. Emblems in panels of previous shield are retained, but in a reduced size. Engraver's initials T.S. flank the lower part of shield. The date flanks the St. Edward's crown. The words A MARI USQUE AD MARE on the ribbon mean "from sea to sea". Horizontal lines in the bottom panel of 1959 issue were removed in 1960. Specifications are identical to 1953- 1958 issues.

Date and Mint Mark	Quantity Minted	VG-8	F-12	VF-20	EF-40	AU-50	MS-60
1959	3,095,535	––	––	––	2.50	3.00	4.50
1960	3,488,897	––	––	––	2.50	3.00	4.00
1961	3,584,417	––	––	––	2.50	3.00	4.00
1962	5,208,030	––	––	––	2.50	3.00	4.00
1963	8,348,871	––	––	––	––	––	3.00
1964	9,377,676	––	––	––	––	––	3.00

MATURE HEAD 1965 -

A new portrait by Arnold Machin depicts a mature draped bust of the Queen wearing a diamond tiara. No change was made in the reverse or the physical specifications.

MS-60 - No traces of wear. High degree of lustre.

Date and Mint Mark	Quantity Minted	VG-8	F-12	VF-20	EF-40	AU-50	MS-60
1965	12,629,974	––	––	––	––	––	3.00
1966	7,683,228	––	––	––	––	––	3.00

The Confederation Centennial reverse design by Alex Colville was a howling wolf. No change was made in the physical specifications.

Date and Mint Mark	Quantity Minted	VF-20	EF-40	AU-50	MS-60
1967	4,211,395	3.00	3.50	4.00	4.50

1968 REDUCED SIZE

In 1968 the diameter and weight were reduced and pure nickel used for the entire issue.

Designers: Obverse - Arnold Machin; Reverse - Thomas Shingles.
Diameter: 27.13 mm; Weight: 8.100 grams; Composition: 1.000 nickel; Reeded edge.

Date and Mint Mark	Quantity Minted	MS-60
1968	3,966,932	1.00
1969	7,113,929	1.00
1970	2,429,516	1.50
1971	2,166,444	1.00
1972	2,515,632	1.00
1973	2,546,096	1.00
1974	3,436,650	1.00
1975	3,710,000	1.00
1976	2,940,719	1.00

THE 1977 REDUCED DESIGN

In 1977 the obverse and reverse design of the fifty cent issue was modified.
The obverse changes included the use of Patrick Brindley's modified Machin bust, a smaller portrait with more detail in the Queen's hair and tiara, smaller lettering in the legend, larger beads farther removed from the rim.
The reverse modifications included a reduced Coat of Arms of Canada, smaller legends with changes in type style, beading replacing the previous rim denticles.

Date and Mint Mark	Quantity Minted	MS-60
1977	709,839	5.00

THE 1978 REVISED DESIGN

The 1978 issue, as in the nickel dollars, has again undergone revision.
The obverse portrait is larger than the 1977 design but slightly smaller than the 1968-1976 portrait. Portrait detail is weak. Beading is smaller and closer to the rim than the 1977 but not equal to the 1968-1976 issue. Lettering in the legends are the same as 1977.
The reverse is a continuation of the 1968-1976 design.

Round Beads   Square Beads

Date and Mint Mark	Quantity Minted	MS-60
1978	3,327,337	.75
1978 Round Beads	Incl.	20.00

Date and Mint Mark	Quantity Minted	MS-60
1979		.75

GEORGE V Silver Jubilee Commemorative 1935

The first Canadian silver dollar issued for circulation commemorated the 25th anniversary of the accession of King George V. It was also the first issue in Canada of a coin to mark a particular event. The special obverse, with the bust carried down to the rim, was in use for this single year. The crowned King is wearing the Robe of State with the Collar of the Garter, fastened by a bow on the shoulder. "ANNO REGNI XXV" means Regnal Year 25.

The reverse design consists of a canoe manned by an Indian and a Voyageur (travelling agent for a fur company), an islet in the background with two trees and incuse lines representing the Northern Lights. The incuse initials H.B. for Hudson's Bay Co. are on the front bundle in the canoe. Designer's initials E.H. at left under canoe. This reverse design has been used on most of Canada's dollar coins.

F-12 - *Jewels in the band of crown will be blurred.*
VF-20 - *Band of crown is still clear but no longer sharp.*
EF-40 - *Band of crown slightly worn but generally sharp and clear, including jewels.*
AU-50 - *Slight traces of wear on high points. Degree of mint lustre still present.*
MS-60 - *No traces of wear. High degree of lustre.*

Designers: Obverse - Percy Metcalfe; Reverse - Emmanuel Hahn.
Diameter: 36.000 mm; Weight: 23.327 grams; Composition: .800 silver, .200 copper; Reeded edge.

Date and Mint Mark	Quantity Minted	F-12	VF-20	EF-40	AU-50	MS-60
1935	428,707	14.00	17.00	20.00	25.00	45.00

GEORGE V Regular Issue 1936

The obverse for 1936 had the regular design for George V as on the cent to fifty cent denominations. The designer's initials B.M. (for Sir E.B. MacKennal) are at the base of the bust. The obverse dies were prepared from the original master die supplied by the Royal Mint in 1911 and used for the pattern dollar that year.

The reverse design, physical specifications and grading are the same as for the 1935 dollar.

Date and Mint Mark	Quantity Minted	F-12	VF-20	EF-40	AU-50	MS-60
1936	306,100	15.00	18.00	21.00	25.00	50.00

Due to shipments from the mint in cardboard tubes of 20, many of the 1935 dollars are of better quality.

Note - Dollar coins of 1935 to 1939 have a duller finish than the 1945 and later issues due to the use of unpolished dies.

GEORGE VI 1937 - 1952

The obverse has the bare-headed portrait of King George VI with designer's initials H.P. under the rear of neck.

The Voyageur reverse of the 1935-1936 issues was retained. This was the only denomination of 1937 coins without a change in reverse design.

F-12 - *Only slight detail in hair above the ear.*
VF-20 - *Where not worn, the hair is clear but not sharp.*
EF-40 - *Slight wear in hair over ear.*
AU-50 - *Slight traces of wear on high points. Degree of mint lustre still present.*
MS-60 - *No traces of wear. High degree of lustre.*

Designers: Obverse - T.H. Paget; Reverse - Emmanuel Hahn.

Diameter: 36.000 mm; Weight: 23.327 grams; Composition: .800 silver, .200 copper; Reeded edge.

Date and Mint Mark	Quantity Minted	F-12	VF-20	EF-40	AU-50	MS-60
1937	241,002	15.00	20.00	25.00	30.00	45.00
1938	90,304	25.00	40.00	50.00	70.00	130.00

ROYAL VISIT 1939

The 1939 silver dollar commemorates the visit of King George VI and Queen Elizabeth to Canada. The reverse shows the centre block of the Parliament Buildings in Ottawa. The obverse legend means "He reigns on the loyality of his people". The designer's initials E.H. were omitted from the dies. To ensure widespread distribution the 1939 dollars were released in the Canadian Post Offices. Approximately 100,000 were melted in 1940.

Reverse Grading

F-12 - *Outline of tower and details of building partly worn away.*
VF-20 - *Wear extends from doorway up the tower and windows and buttresses show wear.*
EF-40 - *Slight wear at the centre of doorway.*
AU-50 - *Slight traces of wear on high points. Degree of mint lustre still present.*
MS-60 - *No traces of wear. High degree of lustre.*

Date and Mint Mark	Quantity Minted	F-12	VF-20	EF-40	AU-50	MS-60
1939	1,363,816	5.00	7.00	9.50	12.00	18.00

VOYAGEUR REVERSE RESUMED 1945

For the first time chromium plated dies were used for the dollar coins and this resulted in a brilliant mint lustre. The reverse design and physical specifications are as for the 1937-1938 issues.

No Silver Dollars Were Struck During The War Years 1940-1944.

Date and Mint Mark	Quantity Minted	F-12	VF-20	EF-40	AU-50	MS-60
1945	38,391	100.00	125.00	150.00	185.00	300.00
1946	93,055	20.00	30.00	40.00	60.00	120.00

Blunt 7

Pointed 7

Maple Leaf

There are three varieties of the 1947 dated silver dollars.
Two of these are classified according to the type of 7 in the date. One has a blunt lower tip and the other a pointed.
A small maple leaf after the 1947 date indicates the coin was struck in 1948.

Date and Mint Mark	Quantity Minted	F-12	VF-20	EF-40	AU-50	MS-60
1947 Blunt 7	65,595	55.00	70.00	90.00	100.00	150.00
*1947 Pointed 7	Incl.	120.00	125.00	175.00	250.00	500.00
1947 Maple Leaf	21,135	125.00	140.00	175.00	225.00	400.00

*Beware of altered Blunt 7.

In 1948 the obverse legend was modified and ET IND: IMP: was omitted. The reverse design and physical specifications remained the same as the previous issues.

Date and Mint Mark	Quantity Minted	F-12	VF-20	EF-40	AU-50	MS-60
1948	18,780	325.00	475.00	575.00	650.00	850.00

NOTE: Choice Uncirculated Dollars have minor abrasions or nicks which were incurred at the Mint either in production, counting and/or shipping. Dollars, as with all decimal coins, were shipped in units of 100's or 1,000's loose in canvas bags, thus making it nearly impossible for coins to arrive at a destination unmarked.

NEWFOUNDLAND ENTRY INTO CONFEDERATION

On December 31, 1949, Newfoundland became a province of the Dominion of Canada. To commemorate the entry of Newfoundland into Confederation, the 1949 reverse design depicts the "Matthew", the ship in which John Cabot is thought to have discovered Newfoundland. Below is the Latin phrase "Floreat Terra Nova" meaning "May the new land flourish". The designer, Thomas Shingles, engraved the master die by hand. His initials appear at the rear of the ship.

The obverse and physical specifications are the same as 1948 issue.

Note: Due to special care in striking, handling and shipping in plastic tubes of 20, many of these dollars are proof-like.

Reverse Grading

F-12 - *Mainsails and shrouds are considerably worn; and motto worn.*
VF-20 - *Extended wear upward along the shrouds from the hull into centre of mainsails.*
EF-40 - *Slight wear on mainsails and shrouds above hull.*
AU-50 - *Slight traces of wear on high points. Degree of mint lustre still present.*
MS-60 - *No traces of wear. High degree of lustre.*

Date and Mint Mark	Quantity Minted	F-12	VF-20	EF-40	AU-50	MS-60
1949	672,218	10.00	18.00	22.00	27.00	32.00

VOYAGEUR REVERSE RESUMED 1950 - 1952

The obverse of the 1948-1949 issue was continued and the Voyageur reverse resumed. Some minor differences exist in the water lines at front end of canoe on the 1950 and 1951 issues and due to the similarity to the 1955 "Arnprior" variety (see text page 65) that descriptive term is used. Some 1950 dollars are without the Northern Lights due to overpolishing of a die.

Date and Mint Mark	Quantity Minted	F-12	VF-20	EF-40	AU-50	MS-60
1950	261,002	10.00	12.00	16.00	20.00	30.00
1950 Arnprior Variety	Incl.	20.00	30.00	35.00	60.00	100.00
1951	416,395	7.00	8.00	10.00	12.00	18.00
1951 Arnprior Variety	Incl.	30.00	45.00	75.00	100.00	150.00

1952 Water Lines   1952 No Water Lines

The usual water lines appear at both ends of the canoe on most of the 1952 dollars and they are the "water lines variety". A smaller quantity with the water lines removed was released and they are the "no water lines variety". No reason was given for the single year issue of the dollar without water lines. Beware of altered waterlines.

Date and Mint Mark	Quantity Minted	F-12	VF-20	EF-40	AU-50	MS-60
1952 Water Lines	406,148	6.50	8.00	9.50	12.00	17.00
1952 No Water Lines	Incl.	9.00	12.00	15.00	20.00	30.00

ELIZABETH II
LAUREATE BUST 1953 - 1964

The obverse depicts a draped laureate bust of Queen Elizabeth II with the Voyageur reverse. The first dies of 1953 had a higher portrait relief than those of George VI and this resulted in unsatisfactory reproduction. The relief was lowered to 3/4 and weaker parts of the design such as hair and shoulder were re-engraved. Early strikings are the "wire edge, no shoulder strap" variety and the later issue were the "flat border, shoulder strap" variety.

Designer's initials: obverse - M.G. at base of bust; reverse - E.H. at left under canoe.

The flat border variety was continued into 1954.

F-12	-	Leaves worn almost through.
VF-20	-	Leaves are considerably worn.
EF-40	-	Laurel leaves on the head are somewhat worn.
AU-50	-	Slight traces of wear on high points. Degree of mint lustre still present.
MS-60	-	No traces of wear. High degree of lustre.

Designer: Obverse - Mrs. Mary Gillick; Reverse - Emmanuel Hahn.

Diameter: 1953 narrow rim - 36.000 mm, 1953 wide rim-1964 - 36.068 mm; Weight: 23.327 grams; Composition: .800 silver, .200 copper; Reeded edge.

Wire Edge   Flat Border

1955 - In December 1955, the Mint made up an order of 2,000 silver dollars for a firm in Arnprior, Ontario, after the regular issue of these coins had been completed for that year. This issue of dollars has only two partial water lines in front of the canoe, instead of the usual three lines. A small quantity of similar dollars, but in proof-like condition were issued late in the year in the sets of coins purchased from the Mint. Similar dollars issued in 1950 and 1951.

There are differences in water lines of other Voyageur dollars too numerous and insignificant to list.

In 1957 there was, in addition to the regular issue, a small quantity with only one water line at the front end of canoe.

Date and Mint Mark	Quantity Minted	F-12	VF-20	EF-40	AU-50	MS-60
1953 Wire Edge, No Shoulder Strap	1,074,578	5.00	6.00	6.50	7.00	8.50
1953 Flat Border, Shoulder Strap	Incl.	5.00	6.00	6.50	7.00	8.50
1954	246,606	7.00	10.00	12.00	14.00	18.00
1955	268,105	7.00	10.00	12.00	14.00	18.00

1950, 1951 & 1955 Arnprior Type Varieties	Regular Water Lines	1957 One Water Line (at right)

Date and Mint Mark	Quantity Minted	F-12	VF-20	EF-40	AU-50	MS-60
1955 Arnprior Variety	2,000	75.00	100.00	125.00	150.00	175.00
1956	209,092	8.00	11.00	13.00	16.00	22.00
1957	496,389	5.00	5.50	6.00	7.00	9.00
1957 One Water Line	Incl.	10.00	14.00	17.00	20.00	30.00

1958 BRITISH COLUMBIA COMMEMORATIVE

To commemorate the gold rush centenary and establishment of British Columbia as an English Crown Colony, a reverse design of an Indian Totem Pole was employed in 1958. The totem pole was used because most of them were made in British Columbia. It was reported that the Indian disliked the coin because a raven appears at the top of the pole. The raven, a carrion bird, is associated with death, and the coin was sometimes referred to as the "death dollar".

Reverse Grading

EF-40 - *Slight wear along the nose of the top face on totem pole.*
AU-50 - *Slight traces of wear of high points. Degree of mint lustre still present.*
MS-60 - *No traces of wear. High degree of lustre.*

Designers: Obverse - Mrs. Mary Gillick; Reverse - Stephen Trenka.

Diameter: 36.068 mm; Weight: 23.327 grams; Composition: .800 silver, .200 copper; Reeded edge.

Date and Mint Mark	Quantity Minted	VF-20	EF-40	AU-50	MS-60
1958 Totem Pole	3,039,630	6.00	6.50	7.00	8.00

VOYAGEUR REVERSE RESUMED 1959 - 1963

Date and Mint Mark	Quantity Minted	VF-20	EF-40	AU-50	MS-60
1959 Canoe Type	1,443,502	––	6.00	6.50	7.00
1960	1,420,486	––	6.00	6.50	7.00
1961	1,262,231	––	6.00	6.50	7.00
1962	1,884,789	––	6.00	6.50	7.00
1963	4,179,981	––	6.00	6.50	7.00

1964 CHARLOTTETOWN COMMEMORATIVE

The special reverse of the 1964 dollar commemorates the 100th anniversary of the Conferences at Charlottetown, P.E.I. and Quebec, Que. of the Fathers of Confederation, which led to Confederation. The design depicts, conjoined within a circle, the French Fleur-de-lis, the Irish shamrock, the Scottish thistle and the English rose. Mr. Dinko Vodanovic won a first prize of $1,000.00 for his design, selected from 169 entered in the competition. The engraver was Thomas Shingles. The initials of both (D.V. and T.S.) appear alongside the inner circle.

Reverse Grading

EF-40 - *Slight wear on flowers in circle.*

AU-50 - *Slight traces of wear on high points. Degree of mint lustre still present.*

MS-60 - *No traces of wear. High degree of lustre.*

Designers: Obverse - Mrs. Mary Gillick; Reverse - D. Vodanovic.

Diameter: 36.068 mm; Weight: 23.327 grams; Composition: .800 silver, .200 copper; Reeded edge.

Date and Mint Mark	Quantity Minted	EF-40	AU-50	MS-60
1964 Charlottetown - Quebec	7,296,832	6.00	6.50	7.00

In 1965 a new obverse was employed, depicting a more mature Queen wearing a tiara. Three obverse varieties exist.

The first has a flat field and small rim beads.

The second has a slightly concave field, medium size rim and minor changes in the portrait, the most distinctive of which is a nearly detached jewel at the back of the Queen's tiara.

The third has a slightly concave field and large beads.

Additionally large and medium bead varieties differ in the positioning of the legend relative to the rim beads. In the large bead variety the apex of letter 'A' in Regina points to a bead. In the small beads variety it points between two beads. The reverse remained the standard Voyageur reverse, but two different 5's, pointed and blunt, were employed. Only a pointed 5 was used with the medium beads variety. The 1965-1966 reverse is similar to earlier Voyageur issues.

Designers: Obverse - Arnold Machin; Reverse - Emmanuel Hahn.

Diameter: 36.068 mm; Weight: 23.327 grams; Composition: .800 silver, .200 copper; Reeded edge.

Small Beads	Pointed 5	Blunt 5

Date and Mint Mark	Quantity Minted	EF-40	AU-50	MS-60
1965 Small Beads, Pointed 5, Variety 1	10,768,569	5.00	5.50	6.00
1965 Small Beads, Blunt 5, Variety 2	Incl.	5.00	5.50	6.00

Large Beads	Blunt 5	Pointed 5

Type 5
Nearly Detached Jewel
At Back Of Queen's Tiara

Date and Mint Mark	Quantity Minted	EF-40	AU-50	MS-60
1965 Large Beads, Blunt 5, Variety 3	Incl.	5.00	5.50	6.00
1965 Large Beads, Pointed 5, Variety 4	Incl.	5.00	5.50	6.00
1965 Medium Beads, Pointed 5, Variety 5	Incl.	15.00	20.00	25.00

Large Beads	Small Beads

A rare variety of the 1966 dollar has small beads. Apparently one of the 1965 obverse dies was used for a very small production. The mintage figure of 485 was obtained from an unofficial but reliable source.

Date and Mint Mark	Quantity Minted	EF-40	AU-50	MS-60
1966 Large Beads	9,912,178	5.00	5.50	6.00
1966 Small Beads	485*	1,000.00	1,100.00	1,300.00

*Unofficial

CENTENNIAL OF CONFEDERATION 1967

In 1967 a special reverse consisting of a Canada Goose in flight was employed to commemorate the 100th anniversary of the Confederation of Provinces to form The Dominion of Canada. A rare variety of the early trial strikes exists with flat fields and the apex of letter 'A' in dollar pointing directly to a bead. On the regular issue the fields are concave and the apex of letter 'A' points between two beads.
The silver dollar represented the last silver dollar issued for circulation.

Designers: Obverse - Arnold Machin; Reverse - Alex Colville.

Diameter: 36.068 mm; Weight: 23.327 grams; Composition: .800 silver, .200 copper; Reeded edge.

Date and Mint Mark	Quantity Minted	EF-40	AU-50	MS-60
1967 Goose (Centennial)	6,767,496	5.50	6.00	7.00

VOYAGEUR REVERSE RESUMED 1968 - 1969

In 1968 the Royal Canadian Mint introduced the all-nickel dollar. This issue was smaller in size and weight. The rapid increase in the world price of silver made the changeover mandatory. Arnold Machin's obverse and Emmanuel Hahn's reverse designs, although reduced, were continued.
Minor varieties known as "No Island" and "Small Island" exist.

Designers: Obverse - Arnold Machin; Reverse - Emmanuel Hahn.

Diameter: 32.131 mm; Weight: 15.616 grams; Composition: 1.000 nickel; Reeded edge.

Date and Mint Mark	Quantity Minted	MS-60
1968 Voyageur Type	5,579,714	1.75
1969 Voyageur Type	4,809,313	1.75

MANITOBA CENTENNIAL 1970

The 1970 reverse commemorates the 100th anniversary of the entry of the province of Manitoba into Confederation. The design depicts two flowers and a bud of the prairie crocus, Manitoba's floral emblem. The designer, Mr. Raymond Taylor, received the first prize of $3,500 for his winning design in national competition. His initial's, R.T., appear at the right of the centre stem. The obverse was continued from the previous year.

Designers: Obverse - Mrs. Mary Gillick; Reverse - Raymond Taylor.
Diameter: 32.131 mm; Weight: 15.616 grams; Composition: 1.000 nickel; Reeded edge.

Date and Mint Mark	Quantity Minted	MS-60
1970 Prairie Crocus, Manitoba Centennial	4,140,058	1.75

BRITISH COLUMBIA CENTENNIAL 1971

In 1971 two different reverse designs were utilized to commemorate the 100th anniversary of the entry of British Columbia into Confederation. The dollar bears on its reverse a combination of the shield which forms part of the coat of arms of British Columbia and two dogwood flowers, the floral emblem of the province. The reverse was designed by Thomas Shingles in open competition. The designer's initials, T.S., are below the shield. The .500 silver "collectors" dollar reverse design is shown on page 82. The 1968-1970 obverse was continued.

Designers: Obverse - Arnold Machin; Reverse - Thomas Shingles.
Diameter: 32.131 mm; Weight: 15.616 grams; Composition: 1.000 nickel; Reeded edge.

Date and Mint Mark	Quantity Minted	MS-60
1971 British Columbia Centennial	4,260,781	1.75

VOYAGEUR REVERSE RESUMED 1972

The obverse and reverse design of the 1972 dollar are a continuation of the 1968-1969 designs. Physical specifications remained the same.

Date and Mint Mark	Quantity Minted	MS-60
1972 Voyageur Type	2,676,041	1.75

PRINCE EDWARD ISLAND CENTENNIAL 1973

The reverse design of the 1973 nickel dollar commemorates the 100th anniversary of the entry of Prince Edward Island into Confederation. The reverse design is a replica of Province House, the Provincial Legislative Building. The winning sketch was by Terry Manning with Walter Ott doing the modelling. Their initials appear at opposite ends of the building, T.M. at left, W.O. at right. This reverse design is the first to carry a bilingual legend and the first nickel dollar to have beads instead of rim denticles. The obverse design is a modification made by Patrick Brindley of Machin's bust of Queen Elizabeth. The Queen's portrait is smaller with more detail in the hair and the jewelled tiara. The beading is larger and removed some distance from the rim which is wider and flatter. The leading jewel in the tiara is attached. See photo page 73.

Designers: Obverse - Arnold Machin; Reverse - Terry Manning & Walter Ott.
Diameter: 32.131 mm; Weight: 15.616 grams; Composition: 1.000 nickel; Reeded edge.

Date and Mint Mark	Quantity Minted	MS-60
1973 Prince Edward Island Centennial	3,196,452	1.75

WINNIPEG CENTENNIAL 1974

The nickel and silver dollars of 1974 commemorate the Centennial Year of the city of Winnipeg. The Winnipeg reverse design was by Paul Pederson with Patrick Brindley again doing the modelling. Their initials appear below and above the large "00's" which also contain two views. In the first "0", a view of Winnipeg's historic corner, Portage and Main, as it was in 1874, with the second "0" as it was in 1974. The obverse is a continuation of the modified 1973 design.

Designers: Obverse - Arnold Machin; Reverse - Paul Pederson & Patrick Brindley.
Diameter: 32.131 mm; Weight: 15.616 grams; Composition: 1.000 nickel; Reeded edge.

Date and Mint Mark	Quantity Minted	MS-60
1974 Winnipeg Centennial	2,799,363	1.75

VOYAGEUR REVERSE RESUMED 1975 - 1976

The obverse modification made by Patrick Brindley on Arnold Machin's design first introduced on nickel dollars in 1973 was continued in 1975.

In 1976 several changes were made to the obverse design; smaller beads aligned closer to the rim, extra wide rims, weakening of detail in the Queen's hair and tiara, the leading jewel on the Queen's tiara is floating free.

The reverse of 1975 and 1976 is a resumption of the 1968-1969 and 1972 design.

No change was made in the physical specifications.

Type 1   Portrait 2   Type 2   Portrait 3

Date and Mint Mark	Quantity Minted	MS-60
1975 Voyageur Type	3,256,000	1.75
1976 Voyageur Type	2,498,204	1.75

VOYAGEUR REVERSE MODIFIED 1977

In 1977 the reverse of the nickel dollar was modified. Emmanuel Hahn's design was revised by Terry Smith, an engraver at the mint. Modification included a smaller design enclosed by wide flat rims with beads replacing the previous rim denticles (matching the obverse). The lettering is smaller and the rays of the northern lights and the designer's initials are raised instead of incused.

The two obverse devices of the past four years are seen for the first time on a single year's issue resulting in two types of nickel dollars for 1977.

Type 1 - The obverse design of 1973-1975 recognized by the attached jewel.

Type 2 - The obverse design of 1976 recognized by the detached jewel.

The reverse is common to both types. However, minor variations do exist due to the removal of various design features in the polishing process of die production. Physical specifications remained the same.

Date and Mint Mark	Quantity Minted	MS-60
1977 Type 1	1,393,745	15.00
1977 Type 2	Incl.	3.00

VOYAGEUR REVERSE MODIFIED 1978

The reverse design of 1978 is nearly full circle from 1977, reverting to the reverse design of 1968-1969 and 1975-1976. However, there are four notable exceptions; raised rays of the northern lights, raised initials for the original designer E. Hahn, new size and type on the date numbers and more detail in cargo carried by the Voyageurs.

The obverse design also has reverted to resemble more closely the original Machin mature head portrait of 1965-1969. The detail in the Queen's hair is weak with the tiara showing slightly more design features than the original but far less than the designs of 1973-1975 and 1976-1977. Physical specifications remained the same.

Date and Mint Mark	Quantity Minted	MS-60
1978	2,920,337	1.60
1979		1.60

Sovereigns

EDWARD VII 1908C - 1910C

Sovereigns were first minted in Canada when a branch of the Royal Mint was opened in Ottawa in 1908. The sovereigns were used as a medium of exchange with Great Britian and Commonwealth Nations that used Pounds Sterling money. The dies were identical to those used by the Royal Mint in London, except fot the 'C' mint mark for Canada above the date. During the First World War the sovereigns were used by England for purchases from the United States, and this avoided the danger of loss at sea for gold shipments across the Atlantic. When Canada took over the Mint as a branch of the Department of Finance of Canada in 1931, the name was changed to the Royal Canadian Mint and the right to mint sovereigns was discontinued. Many of the sovereigns were melted and cast in bars, so the mintage figures are not a guide to rarity. All of the 1908C were originally Specimens, but some got into circulation.

F-12 - *Little detail in hair above ear and the beard is considerably worn.*
VF-20 - *Wear on head spreads near the ear and slight wear develops on the beard.*
EF-40 - *Hair over ear is only slightly worn. Beard is still sharp.*
AU-50 - *Faint trace of wear on beard and hair. Some lustre remains.*
MS-60 - *No wear showing. Mint lustre retained.*

Designers: Obverse - G.W. DeSaulles; Reverse - Benedetto Pistrucci.

Diameter: 22.05 mm; Weight: 7.988 grams; Composition: .917 gold, .083 copper; Reeded edge.

Date and Mint Mark	Quantity Minted	F-12	VF-20	EF-40	AU-50	MS-60
1908C	636	800.00	1,200.00	1,600.00	1,750.00	2,000.00
1909C	16,273	100.00	125.00	175.00	200.00	250.00
1910C	28,012	100.00	125.00	175.00	200.00	250.00

GEORGE V 1911C - 1919C

F-12 - *Little detail in hair above ear and the beard is considerably worn.*
VF-20 - *Wear on head spreads near the ear and slight wear develops on the beard.*
EF-40 - *Hair over ear is only slightly worn. Beard is still sharp.*
AU-50 - *Faint trace of wear on beard and hair. Some lustre remains.*
MS-60 - *No wear showing. Mint lustre retained.*

Designers: Obverse - Sir E.B. MacKennal; Reverse - Benedetto Pistrucci.

Diameter: 22.05 mm; Weight: 7.988 grams or .2354 Troy ounces; Composition: .917 gold, .083 copper; Reeded edge.

The 1916C is by far the rarest and it is believed that the vast majority of these sovereigns were melted and cast in bars. Less than ten are known to exist today.

Date and Mint Mark	Quantity Minted	F-12	VF-20	EF-40	AU-50	MS-60
1911C	256,946	80.00	90.00	95.00	100.00	110.00
1913C	3,715	400.00	500.00	700.00	875.00	1,100.00
1914C	14,891	125.00	175.00	225.00	250.00	275.00
1916C	6,111	7,000.00	10,000.00	13,000.00	14,500.00	16,000.00
1917C	58,845	85.00	95.00	100.00	105.00	115.00
1918C	106,516	85.00	95.00	100.00	105.00	115.00
1919C	135,889	85.00	95.00	100.00	105.00	115.00

5 & 10 Dollars

GEORGE V 1912 - 1914

5 DOLLARS

The gold coins which first appeared in 1912 show the Arms of Canada on a square shield superimposed on two branches of maple. The Arms were the combined Arms of the Provinces of Ontario, Quebec, Nova Scotia and New Brunswick. These four provinces merged together to form the Dominion of Canada in 1867. The Arms of the provinces are: Ontario - a twig of maple leaves below the cross of St. George; Quebec - two fleur-de-lis above, lion in centre and a twig of three maple leaves below; Nova Scotia - two thistles above, salmon in centre and one thistle below; New Brunswick - an ancient galley with oars in action and a lion above.

F-12 - *Jewels in the band of crown will be blurred.*
VF-20 - *Band of crown is still clear but no longer sharp.*
EF-40 - *Band of crown is slightly worn but generally sharp and clear.*
AU-50 - *Faint trace of wear on high points. Some mint lustre is remaining.*
MS-60 - *No wear showing. All details sharp and clear. Mint lustre retained.*

Designers: Obverse - Sir E.B. MacKennal; Reverse - W.H.J. Blakemore.

Diameter: 21.590 mm; Weight: 8.359 grams; Composition: .900 gold, .100 copper; Reeded edge.

Date and Mint Mark	Quantity Minted	F-12	VF-20	EF-40	AU-50	MS-60
1912	165,680	100.00	150.00	175.00	210.00	240.00
1913	98,832	110.00	160.00	185.00	220.00	250.00
1914	31,122	300.00	425.00	525.00	575.00	650.00

GEORGE V 1912 - 1914

10 DOLLARS

F-12 - *Jewels in the band of crown will be blurred.*
VF-20 - *Band of crown is still clear but no longer sharp.*
EF-40 - *Band of crown is slightly worn but generally sharp and clear.*
AU-50 - *Faint trace of wear on high points. Some mint lustre is remaining.*
MS-60 - *No wear showing. All details sharp and clear. Mint lustre retained.*

Designers: Obverse - Sir E.B. MacKennal; Reverse - W.H.J. Blakemore.

Diameter: 26.924 mm; Weight: 16.718 grams; Composition: .900 gold, .100 copper; Reeded edge.

Date and Mint Mark	Quantity Minted	F-12	VF-20	EF-40	AU-50	MS-60
1912	74,759	225.00	375.00	450.00	525.00	600.00
1913	149,232	225.00	375.00	450.00	525.00	650.00
1914	140,068	250.00	425.00	500.00	575.00	700.00

20 DOLLARS
CANADA CENTENNIAL - 1967

In 1967 to commemorate the Canadian Centennial a $20.00 Centennial gold coin was struck. It is the only coin of the Centennial series that does not have the dates 1867-1967.
This denomination was released only in the black leather presentation cased set of Centennial coins, which sold for $40.00. It is of "specimen" quality.
The obverse was the current design of Queen Elizabeth II, and the reverse was an adaption of the Canadian Coat of Arms used on the 50 cent coin of 1959.

Designers: Obverse - Arnold Machin; Reverse - Myron Cook.

Diameter: 27.050 mm; Weight: 18.723 grams or .5287 troy ounces; Composition: .900 gold, .100 copper; Reeded edge.

Mintage - 337,688 . . . . $175.00

100 DOLLARS
OLYMPIC GOLD COINS - 1976

To commemorate and help finance the 21st Olympic Games, two $100.00 Olympic gold coins were issued. The 14 carat uncirculated coin was encased in a card holder while the 22 carat proof edition was released in a case of tanned steerhide and maple with a rosewood finish. The uncirculated coin is slightly larger and has obverse rim beads, which are not on the proof coin. The reverse of the $100.00 Canadian Olympic gold coin was designed by the Canadian medallic artist, Dora de Pedery-Hunt. The reverse bears the standing figure of the goddess Athena. Her left hand is on the shoulder of an athlete who is carrying the victor's garland and sash. Below the feet of the two figures appears the Greek word for "Olympiad" and below the word, the Arabic figures "21".

UNCIRCULATED 14 CARAT	PROOF 22 CARAT
.5833 fine	.9166 fine
1976 with beads	1976 no beads

Designers: Obverse - Arnold Machin; Reverse - Dora de Pedery-Hunt.

Uncirculated 14k: Diameter: 27 mm; Weight: 13.3375 grams; Composition: 14 carat with a pure gold content of 7.7759 grams.

Proof 22k: Diameter: 25 mm; Weight: 16.9655 grams; Composition: 22 carat with a pure gold content of 15.5517 grams.

14Kt Unc. Mintage - 572,387 . . . . . . $110.00
22Kt Proof Mintage - 335,779 . . . . . . $165.00

100 DOLLARS
ELIZABETH II SILVER JUBILEE - 1977

A $100.00 gold coin was struck to commemorate the 25th anniversary of the accession to the throne of Queen Elizabeth II.
The reverse design by Toronto artist Raymond Lee depicts the official flowers of Canada's provinces and territories. The obverse bears Arnold Machin's protrait of the Queen and the inscription "Silver Jubilee - Elizabeth II 1952-1977 - 25 ans de regne".

Diameter: 27 mm; Weight: 16.5885 grams; Composition: .91667 gold, .08333 silver.

Mintage - 180,396 $300.00

100 DOLLARS
UNITY 1978

Artist Roger Savage of Nova Scotia designed the reverse of this $100.00 gold coin, struck in Proof, showing a graceful flight of twelve Canada Geese meant to represent the ten Canadian provinces and two territories. Their strength, beauty and interdependance symbolize the unity of Canada. The obverse bears Arnold Machin's regal effigy of the Queen and the legend "100 Dollars Canada 1978 Elizabeth II".

Diameter: 27 mm; Weight: 16.965 grams; Composition: .9166 gold, .0834 silver.

Mintage - 200,000 $190.00

100 DOLLARS
INTERNATIONAL YEAR OF THE CHILD - 1979

A $100.00 gold coin will be struck to honour the United Nations "Year of the Child". These coins are struck in Proof condition. The reverse design by Carala Tietz of Ottawa depicts children of different nationalities, playing hand in hand around the earth, getting to know each other, thus contributing to world unity. The obverse bears Machin's portrait of the Queen.

Diameter: 27 mm; Weight: 16.965 grams; Composition: .9166 gold, .0834 silver.

Mintage - $190.00

COINS OF CANADA

MINT SETS

Prior to 1953 the Ottawa agency of the Bank of Canada accepted orders for Uncirculated coin sets at face value plus postage and registration. Early in 1953 the Royal Canadian Mint assumed this responsibility and offered to supply sets of coins dated 1951, 1952 and 1953 in cellophane envelopes at $2.25 for the 1951 (with both nickels) and $2.20 each for the 1952 and 1953. After stapling the envelopes together, the sets were packed and sealed in little white cardboard boxes. For an additional ten cents each, the sets would be supplied in cardboard holders with cellophane covers. These prices represented only the face value of coins, plus the cost of containers and registered postage. The coins in these mint sets were for the most part production strikes, but due to a minimum of handling and possibly some selection, the quality was generally superior to the regular issue, particularily those of 1950, 1951 and 1952. A few selected coins from these sets could be termed Proof-like, but complete sets are rare.

There was a huge demand for the 1953 coin sets due to the Coronation year coinage of Queen Elizabeth II and the quality of the 1953 mint sets soon deteriorated until it was generally little better than bag Uncirculated.

Although there are no official figures covering the sale of these mint sets, a clue to the totals may be found in the Mint Report listings of coins issues to Sundry Persons.

The following yearly sales are indicated: 1950 - 108; 1951 - 960; 1952 - 2,317; 1953 - 15,779.

PROOF-LIKE MINT SETS AND DOLLARS

Proof-like coins have a brilliant mirror-like finish and are free of handling abrasions. New dies, which are frequently replaced, are used, the planchets are thoroughly washed and the coins are carefully struck on slow moving presses. The operators are required to wear clean gloves and the coins are carefully scrutinized prior to packaging. Although the Mint sells the packaged sets as Uncirculated coins, the term Proof-like is universally used as it is more descriptive, particularily in distinguishing these coins from regular production strikes with customary bag abrasions. Due to their superior finish the Proof-like coins are sometimes mistakenly classed as Specimens or Proofs. It should be noted that Proof-like coins are not as sharply struck and the higher denominations often have a slight roughness at the Queen's shoulder because they are single struck with less striking pressure. Proofs and Specimens are usually double struck under much greater pressure which results in a flawless surface, sharp wire edge and better detail.

The history of the Proof-like sets really began on September 4, 1953, the day of the C.N.A. annual meeting and election of officers in Ottawa. As part of the program, a visit to the Mint was arranged and the opportunity given to members to purchase sets of coins of the current year prepared for the occasion. The condition of these coin sets was of such a high quality and with some Proof characteristics, a new descriptive term was required and this resulted in Proof-like being used for the first time when one of the sets was listed in the author's November 21, 1953 auction sale catalogue. The 1954 and later Mint issue sets were comparable in quality, so the descriptive term has continued in use.

All the so-called Uncirculated coin sets purchased by the Royal Canadian Mint from 1954 to date are in Proof-like condition although the quality was somewhat inferior in 1965 and 1968. In 1965 the huge increase in production was no doubt a factor, as was the change to nickel coinage in 1968.

Practically all Uncirculated coin sets purchased from the Mint prior to 1954 are nothing more than Choice Uncirculated and the fact that the coins came directly from the Mint is of no significance. The author probably purchased more of these sets than anyone else during the 1950-1953 period and so had an excellent opportunity to examine them.

The few 1953 "shoulder strap" and "no shoulder strap" Proof-like sets that exist were probably obtained at the time of the Mint visit. The author knows of none received by mail.

Issue prices of Proof-like sets: 1953 - $2.20; 1954-1959 - $2.50; 1960-1964 - $3.00; 1965-1973 - $4.00; 1974-1976 - $5.00; 1977 - $5.15; 1978 - $5.25.

Proof-like Dollars: 1955-1964 - $1.25; 1965-1967 - no issue; 1968-1969 - $1.25; 1970-1973 (cased) - $2.00; 1975-1976 (cased) - $2.50.

Proof-like sets minted from 1953 to 1960 inclusive were issued in white cardboard holders within cellophane envelopes. In 1960 only, the holder was imprinted ROYAL CANADIAN MINT, OTTAWA, CANADA. From 1961 to date, the sets have been released in sealed pliofilm envelopes embossed with the words "ROYAL CANADIAN MINT".

Proof-like dollars were not officially issued in the following years: 1953, 1965-1967, 1977, 1978 and are only available from P.L. sets.

This type issued 1953 to 1960

This type issued 1961 to date

Date and Mint Mark	Quantity Minted	Sets (6 coins)	Date and Mint Mark	Quantity Minted	P.L. Dolla
†1953 NSS		900.00	1950		150.00
†1953 SS		900.00	1951		140.00
1954	7,426*	300.00	1952 NWL		170.00
1954 Strapless Cent	Incl.	350.00	1953 NSS		400.00
1955	6,301*	165.00	1953 SS		400.00
1955 Arnprior	Incl.	325.00	1954	1.268*	180.00
1956	9,018*	125.00	1955	5,501*	100.00
1957	11,862*	50.00	1955 Arnprior	Incl.	250.00
1958 Totem Pole	18,259	50.00	1956	6,154*	60.00
1959	31,577	20.00	1957	4,379*	30.00
1960	64,097	17.00	1958 Totem Pole	14,978*	30.00
1961	98,373	15.00	1959	13,583	12.00
1962	200,950	8.50	1960	18,631	9.0
1963	673,006	8.00	1961	22,555	8.00
1964 Charlottetown Conference	1,653,162	8.00	1962	47,951	6.00
1965 With Pointed 5 Dollar	2,904,352	8.00	1963	290,529	5.50
1965 With Blunt 5 Dollar	Incl.	8.00	1964 Charlottetown Conference	1,209,279	5.5
1966	672,514	8.00	1965 Type 1		5.5
			1965 Type 2		5.5
			1965 Type 3		150.00
			1965 Type 4		90.0
			1966		4.5

*Estimate

†The vast majority of mint sets and silver dollars dated before 1954 are not in Proof-like condition, even though obtained from the Royal Canadian Mint.
This is particularly the case with the 1953 issue. 1953 P.L. Sets price range from $700.00 to $900.00.

Date and Mint Mark	Quantity Minted	Sets (6 coins)	Date and Mint Mark	Quantity Minted	P.L. Dollar
1967 Canadian Cent.	963,714	11.00	1967 Canadian Cent.		7.50
1968 1st Nickel Dollar			1968 1st Nickel Dollar		
Small Size	521,641	3.50	Small Size	885,124	2.00
1969	326,203	4.00	1969	221,112	2.00
1970 Manitoba Cent.	349,120	11.50	1970 Manitoba Cent.	297,547	4.00
1971 B.C. Cent.	253,311	7.00	1971 B.C. Cent.	181,901	4.00
1972 Voyageur	224,275	5.00	1972 Voyageur	143,392	3.75
1973 P.E.I. Cent.			1973 P.E.I. Cent.	173,810	3.50
Small Bust 25¢	243,695	6.50	1974 Winnipeg Cent.	105,901	4.00
1973 Large Bust 25¢	Incl.	225.00	1975 Voyageur	88,102	4.00
1974 Winnipeg Cent.	213,589	7.00	1976 Voyageur	74,207	5.00
1975 Voyageur	197,372	7.00	1977 Voyageur		5.00
1976 Voyageur	171,737	13.00	1978 Voyageur		4.00
1977 Voyageur	225,307	14.00	1979 Voyageur		4.00
1978 Voyageur		7.00			
1979 Voyageur		7.00			

CASED CUSTOM SETS

In 1971 the Mint introduced the "custom" set of 7 coins. An attractive simulated leather case displays the reverse design of the nickel dollar and the other coins from 1¢ to 50¢. An additional 1¢ coin shows the obverse design. The coins are of Proof-like quality.

Date and Mint Mark	Quantity Minted	
1971 B.C. Centennial	33,517	10.00
1972 Voyageur	38,198	10.00
1973 P.E.I. Centennial	49,376	10.00
1974 Winnipeg Centennial	44,296	10.00
1975 Voyageur	36,851	10.00
1976 Voyageur	28,162	16.00
1977 Voyageur	44,198	20.00
1978 Voyageur		12.00
1979 Voyageur		12.00

CASED SILVER DOLLARS
Non-Circulating

In 1971 the Royal Canadian Mint commenced striking .500 fine silver dollars for distribution to collectors. None are released for circulation. These dollars are the same size and weight as the pre-1968 dollars. They are double struck of specimen quality and sold in presentation cases. Apart from the 1972 issue, they commemorate historical events in Canada's history.

BRITISH COLUMBIA CENTENNIAL 1971

This silver dollar commemorates the 100th anniversary of the entry of British Columbia into Confederation. The obverse portrait is a modification by Patrick Brindley of the original Machin design and shows greater hair detail.
The reverse bears a modified version of the full coat of arms of the province.

Designers: Obverse - Arnold Machin; Reverse - Patrick Brindley.

1971 British Columbia Centennial . . . . Mintage - 555,564 . . . . 14.00

VOYAGEUR REVERSE 1972

Designers: Obverse - Arnold Machin; Reverse - Emmanuel Hahn.

1972 Voyageur . . . . Mintage - 350,109 . . . . 13.00

ROYAL CANADIAN MOUNTED POLICE CENTENNIAL 1973

The 100th anniversary of the Royal Canadian Mounted Police is commemorated on the 1973 silver dollar. The reverse depicts a mounted member of the North West Mounted Police on patrol at the turn of the century. The design was by Paul Cedarberg and it was modeled and engraved by Patrick Brindley. The initials of both men are on the coin.
The obverse design of the previous year was retained.

Designers: Obverse - Arnold Machin; Reverse - Paul Cedarberg & Patrick Brindley.

1973 Royal Canadian Mounted Police Centennial . . . Mintage - 904,795 . . . .   8.00
1973 R.C.M.P., with metal crest on the box . . . . Mintage - Incl. 30.00

WINNIPEG CENTENNIAL 1974

The 1974 silver dollar commemorated the centennial of the City of Winnipeg. The reverse design depicts two views of the historic corner of Portage Avenue and Main Street. One as it appeared in 1874 and the other in 1974. The design was by Paul Pederson, and Patrick Brindley modeled the reverse. Their initials appear below and above the large "100".

Designers: Obverse - Arnold Machin; Reverse - Paul Pederson & Patrick Brindley.

1974 Winnipeg Centennial . . . . Mintage - 628,183 . . . .   6.00

CALGARY CENTENNIAL 1975

1975 was the centennary of the City of Calgary and to mark the occasion a silver dollar was issued. A competition was held and from approximately 500 entries the design submitted by Donald D. Paterson was chosen. This design depicts a rider and horse competing in the world famous Calgary Stampede. Oil wells and a modern city skyline appear in the background. Patrick Brindley modeled the reverse and the initials of both men are on the coin. No change was made in the obverse design.

Designers: Obverse - Arnold Machin; Reverse - Donald D. Paterson; Patrick Brindley.

1975 City of Calgary Centennial . . . . Mintage - 833,095 . . . . 5.00

PARLIAMENT LIBRARY CENTENNIAL 1976

The 1976 silver dollar commemorates the 100th anniversary of the completion of the construction of the Library of Parliament Building. The reverse design was modeled by Walter Ott and his name monogram appears at the lower right. Patrick Brindley was the engraver and his initial is at the lower left. The obverse portrait remained unchanged.

Designers: Obverse - Arnold Machin; Reverse - Walter Ott & Patrick Brindley.

1976 Parliament Library Centennial . . . . Mintage - 483,722 . . . . 9.00
1976 as above, in V.I.P. case with metal crest . . . . . . Mintage - Incl. 39.00

ELIZABETH JUBILEE 1977

The 25th anniversary of Queen Elizabeth's accession to the throne is commemorated with the 1977 silver dollar. The reverse depicts the Throne of the Senate of Canada. The Throne is used by the Queen and her representative, the Governor General, on ceremonial occassions, such as the opening of Parliament. No change was made in the obverse design.

Designers: Obverse - Arnold Machin; Reverse - Raymond Lee.

1977 Senate Throne . . . . Mintage - 744,848 . . . . 8.00

XI COMMONWEALTH GAMES 1978

This silver dollar commemorated the XI Commonwealth Games which were held in the City of Edmonton, Alberta, August 3-12, 1978. The reverse of the coin features the Commonwealth Games' symbol in the centre and along its perimeter the official symbols of the ten sports which comprise the Commonwealth Games. The design was by Toronto artist Raymond Taylor.

Designers: Obverse - Arnold Machin; Reverse - Raymond Taylor.

1978 XI Commonwealth Games . . . . Mintage - 709,602 . . . . 6.00

300th ANNIVERSARY 1979

This silver dollar commemorates the 300th anniversary of the first voyage by a commercial ship "The Griffon" on the Great Lakes, upstream of Niagara Falls. The reverse features the ship, Griffon, in full sail. The designer is Walter Schluep of Montreal.

Designers: Obverse - Arnold Machin; Reverse - Walter Schluep.

1979 Griffon . . . . Mintage - $6.00

CASED CENTENNIAL SETS 1867 - 1967
GOLD PRESENTATION SET

On the first of July 1867, the four provinces of Ontario, Quebec, New Brunswick and Nova Scotia united to become the Dominion of Canada. In 1967 to mark the 100th anniversary of the Confederation of Canada, the Royal Canadian Mint produced a Presentation Coin Set containing a $20.00 gold coin. This coin was not issued separately.

The Coat of Arms of Canada, as introduced on the 50 cents of 1959, appears on the reverse of the $20.00 gold coin and the Arnold Machin design of Queen Elizabeth II on the obverse. In addition to the $20.00 gold coin, the set contains six subsidiary coins from one dollar to one cent, bearing the Centennial reverse designs. The seven coins, all "specimens", are enclosed in a black genuine morocco leather presentation case and the issue price was $40.00 per set.

1967 Centennial - 1¢, 5¢, 10¢, 25¢, 50¢, $1.00, $20.00 (337,688) 180.00

SILVER MEDALLION PRESENTATION SET

This 1967 set contains a sterling silver medallion approximately 1½ inches in diameter. The obverse design depicts the Canadian Shield and the reverse bears the design of the Canadian Symbol. In addition, the set contains the six subsidiary coins from one dollar to one cent bearing the Centennial reverse designs, with obverse portrait of Queen Elizabeth II.

The medallion and six coins are encased in a red, genuine Canadian cowhide leather presentation case. Issue price was $12.00 per set.

1967 Centennial - 1¢, 5¢, 10¢, 25¢, 50¢, $1.00, silver medallion. 20.00

CASED DOUBLE DOLLAR SETS

In 1971 and 1972 the Mint issued 7 coin presentation sets containing one coin of each denomination, together with an extra dollar. Both dollars were nickel, and all coins were double struck. The issue price was $12.00 per set. Commencing in 1973, the .500 silver dollar replaced the extra nickel dollar.

These sets have become yearly issues and the current presentation set features the encapsulated set held in a plastic frame, permitting a view of both sides of the coins. The genuine leather case is satin lined, and has a three dimensional silver plated oxidized casting of the Canadian Coat of Arms on the cover.

Date			Issue Price	
1971 - 7 coins (2-$1.00 coins)	66,860	. . . .	12.00	25.00
1972 - 7 coins (2-$1.00 coins)	36,349	. . . .	12.00	65.00
1973 - 7 coins (2-$1.00 coins)	119,891	. . . .	12.00	21.00
1974 - 7 coins (2-$1.00 coins)	85,230	. . . .	12.00	21.00
1975 - 7 coins (2-$1.00 coins)	97,263	. . . .	12.00	21.00
1976 - 7 coins (2-$1.00 coins)	87,744	. . . .	16.00	35.00
1977 - 7 coins (2-$1.00 coins)	142,577	. . . .	16.50	45.00
1978 - 7 coins (2-$1.00 coins)		. . . .	16.50	22.00
1979 - 7 coins (2-$1.00 coins)		. . . .	18.50	24.50

OLYMPIC COINS 1973 - 1976

In 1976 Canada hosted the Olympic Games. To commemorate and help finance Canada's first Olympics, the Royal Canadian Mint struck 28 different sterling silver, legal tender coins. (Also two varieties of a $100 gold coin listed on page 75). The silver coins, in 7 series of 4 coins each, consisted of two $5.00 and two $10.00 coins, depicting Olympic scenery on the reverse and Arnold Machin's bust of Queen Elizabeth II on the obverse. The coins were struck at the Hull branch of the Royal Canadian Mint from 1973 to 1976. The obverse date in each case was the release date and usually the year of minting.

Orders for the Olympic coins were accepted up to the end of December 1976, so a small unit continued to function into 1977 on the Olympic Coin Program.

During the striking of Series I 1973 $10.00 coins, an obverse die was removed from one of the presses and a Series II 1974 obverse die was inserted for test purposes. After completion of the test, the obverse 1974 die was inadvertently left in the press and production resumed with the $10.00 coin dated 1974 on the obverse and the map of the 1973 issue on the reverse. Some hundreds of the error coins are now in the hands of collectors.

The vast majority of the Olympic coins were encapsulated or in presentation cases. An exception was nearly a million of Series I unencapsulated released through the banks and other financial institutions at face value. Only small quantities of the other series were sold unencapsulated. The sets of four coins were available in three different presentation cases: custom (red lining), prestige (blue lining), and the proof set in a case of Canadian white birch and tanned steerhide.

The bust of Queen Elizabeth II used on all Olympic coins was the Patrick Brindley modification of Arnold Machin's design.

$5.00 Coin: Diameter: 38 mm; Weight: 24.30 grams; Silver Content: .925 fine silver (.723 troy ounces); Reeded edge.

$10.00 Coin: Diameter: 45 mm; Weight: 48.60 grams; Silver Content: .925 fine silver (1.44 troy ounces); Reeded edge.

SERIES I - ISSUED 1973
GEOGRAPHIC

Designer: George Huel

$10.00 - Map of the World

Canada is highlighted as the host nation.

No. 1 MS-60 . . . . $ 15.00
1974 Obverse Error, MS-60 . . . . . $400.00

$5.00 - Map of North America

No. 2 Canada is hightlighted as the host nation.

MS-60 . . . . $ 7.50

$10.00 - Skyline of Montreal

No. 3 The skyline of Montreal, host city to the XXI Olympiad.

MS-60 . . . . $ 15.00

$5.00 - Racing Sailboats

No. 4 Landmarks of Kingston, the host city for the yachting events, in background.

MS-60 . . . . $ 7.50

CASED 4-COIN SETS

Custom: $45.00; Prestige: $45.00; Proof: $60.00

SERIES II - ISSUED 1974
OLYMPIC MOTIFS

Designer: Anthony Mann

$10.00 - Head of Zeus

No. 5   The mythical father of ancient Greek gods, to whom the original Olympics were dedicated.

MS-60 . . . . $16.00

$5.00 - Athlete with Torch

No. 6   Symbolizes the constant rebirth of the Olympics.

MS-60 . . . . $9.00

$10.00 - Temple of Zeus

No. 7   Home of the Statue of Zeus, one of the seven wonders of the ancient world and temporal focal point of the early games.

MS-60 . . . . $16.00

$5.00 - Olympic Rings & Wreath

No. 8   Features the ancient Olympic victor's crown and the 5-ring symbol, now representing the five continents and man's interlocking friendship.

MS-60 . . . . $9.00

CASED 4-COIN SETS

Custom: $50.00; Prestige: $50.00; Proof: $65.00

SERIES III - ISSUED 1974
EARLY CANADIAN SPORTS

Designer: Ken Danby

$10.00 - Lacrosse

No. 9

Lacrosse, a sport developed by the Indians before the voyage of Columbus, became so popular in Canada that it was declared Canada's official sport in 1867.

MS-60 . . . . $16.00

$5.00 - Canoeing

No. 10

Canoeing in Canada's early days was often the only mode of transportation over the inland waterways. It was also featured in competitions between Voyageurs and Indians.

MS-60 . . . . $9.00

$10.00 - Cycling

No. 11

Cycling was an extremely popular sport in Canada in the 1870's. The first cycling club in Canada was in Montreal, site of the 1976 Olympic Games.

MS-60 . . . . $16.00

$5.00 - Rowing

No. 12

The first Canadian athlete to be crowned World Champion was sculler Ned Hanlan of Toronto. The regatta in St. John's, Nfld. is the oldest continuously competed sporting event in North America.

MS-60 . . . . $9.00

CASED 4-COIN SETS

Custom: $50.00; Prestige: $50.00; Proof: $80.00

SERIES IV - ISSUED 1975
OLYMPIC TRACK & FIELD SPORTS

Designer: Leo Yerxa

$10.00 - Men's Hurdles

No. 13   The Indian quill-work depicts wild deer jumping over fallen trees in the forest symbolizing the fluid motion of the hurdler.

MS-60 . . . . $16.00

$5.00 - The Marathon

No. 14   Two stylized birds in migratory flight symbolize the stamina of a participant in the marathon.

MS-60 . . . . $9.00

$10.00 - Ladies' Shot Put

No. 15   The flame of the sun and the arc of its passage through the sky depicts the flight and distance of the shot.

MS-60 . . . . $16.00

$5.00 - Ladies' Javelin

No. 16   The Indian spear heads in the quill-work idiom trace the direction and flight of the javelin.

MS-60 . . . . $9.00

CASED 4-COIN SETS

Custom: $50.00; Prestige: $50.00; Proof: $80.00

SERIES V - ISSUED 1975
OLYMPIC WATER SPORTS

Designer: Linda Cooper

$10.00 - The Paddler

No. 17   The three Olympic paddling events; rowing, canoeing and kayaking are symbolized by a single figure pitted against time, pressure and fatigue. A watercourse swirls around him.

MS-60 . . . . $18.00

$5.00 - The Diver

No. 18   The graceful woman diver is shown passing through a time lapse sequence before completing her dive.

MS-60 . . . . $9.50

$10.00 - Sailing

No. 19   The co-ordinated teamwork of two sailors is symbolized - one at the tiller, the other straining to counterbalance the thrust of the wind. Distant sails on the horizon.

MS-60 . . . . $18.00

$5.00 - The Swimmer

No. 20   The refracted image of a swimmer in competition echoes the heaving turbulence of the water.

MS-60 . . . . $9.50

CASED 4-COIN SETS

Custom: $55.00; Prestige: $55.00; Proof: $85.00

SERIES VI - ISSUED 1976
OLYMPIC TEAM & BODY CONTACT SPORTS

Designer: Shigeo Fukuda

The designs portray Olympic Team & Body Contact sports. In each the silhouette of athletes in Olympic competition stands out against a background representing a sunburst- the repeated silhouette effect providing unity of flow in all directions.

No. 21 $10.00 - Field Hockey

MS-60 . . . . $18.00

No. 22 $5.00 - Fencing

MS-60 . . . . $9.50

No. 23 $10.00 - Football

MS-60 . . . . $18.00

No. 24 $5.00 - Boxing

MS-60 . . . . $9.50

CASED 4-COIN SETS

Custom: $55.00; Prestige: $55.00; Proof: $85.00

SERIES VII - ISSUED 1976
OLYMPIC SOUVENIR SERIES

Designer: Elliott Morrison

$10.00 - Olympic Stadium

No. 25   The location of track & field, swimming, and other events as well as the ceremonial opening and closing.

MS-60 . . . . $25.00

$5.00 - Olympic Village

No. 26   This spectacular building provided housing for the athletes.

MS-60 . . . . $12.50

$10.00 - Olympic Velodrome

No. 27   The scene of most cycling and judo events.

MS-60 . . . . $25.00

$5.00 - Olympic Flame

No. 28   The flame was lit at the opening ceremonies, July 17, 1976, and was extinguished at the closing ceremonies, August 1st.

MS-60 . . . . $12.50

CASED 4-COIN SETS

Custom: $75.00; Prestige: $75.00; Proof: $100.00

Prior to 1967 the Ottawa Mint struck specimen sets for sale to the public only in the years 1908, 1911 & 1937. These are often incorrectly referred to as "proof sets" and consist of double-struck coins with unusually sharp detail, and either a matte or a brilliant, mirror-like surface.

Only a few Canadian specimen sets and other specimen coins were struck in other years at the Ottawa Mint, Tower Mint London, and Heaton Mint in Birmingham. They are rare and seldom change hands.

This listing is compiled basically from sets actually handled by the author and members of the panel in recent years. It is realized that other sets are in existance and additions to this list will be made in the next edition of this catalogue upon completion of research.

NOTE: To distinguish specimen from proof-like coins, look for sharpness of detail and smooth surface, particularily at the Queen's shoulder on recent issues, also square edge and rim, and full reeding.

Sets In Cases Unless Stated Otherwise
Values Of Sets Without Cases For This Period Are $200.00 Less

1858	Victoria - 1¢, 5¢, 10¢, 20¢, small date 5¢ piece	$ 4,000.00
1858	Victoria - 1¢, 5¢, 10¢, 20¢, large date 5¢ piece.	$ 5,000.00
1858	Victoria Double Sets - 1¢, 5¢, 10¢, 20¢.	$ 8,000.00
1870	Victoria - 5¢, 10¢, 25¢, 50¢	$ 6,000.00
1908	Edward VII - 1¢, 5¢, 10¢, 25¢, 50¢ (1,000 issued)	$ 1,000.00
1911	George V - 1¢, 5¢, 10¢, 25¢, 50¢, (1,000 issued)	$ 3,500.00
1911	George V - 1¢, 5¢, 10¢, 25¢, 50¢, plus gold sovereign 1911C and	
	1912 $5 & $10 gold (probably only 5 50 10 sets exist) . . .	$13,000.00

1921	George V - 1¢, 5¢, 10¢, 25¢, 50¢, without case. Silver has semi-matte surface, bronze cent semi-brilliant; square edges	$50,000.00
1929	George V - 1¢, 5¢, 10¢, 25¢, 50¢. Silver has brilliant surface, 5¢ piece has matte surface, cent is semi-brilliant; square edges	$ ────
1934	George V - 1¢, 5¢, 10¢, 25¢, 50¢, without case. Silver has semi-matte surface, bronze cent semi-brilliant; square edges	$ 5,000.00
1936	George V - 1¢, 5¢, 10¢, 25¢, 50¢. Silver has a matte surface, 5¢ piece a matte surface, bronze cent semi-brilliant; square edges	$ 5,500.00
1937	George VI - 1¢ to $1.00, coins brilliant; leather mint case	$ 1,200.00
1937	George VI - 1¢ to $1.00, coins semi-matte; leather mint case	$ 900.00
1937	George VI - 1¢ to $1.00, coins brilliant; card case.	$ 900.00
1937	George VI - 1¢ to $1.00, coins semi-matte; card case	$ 500.00
1937	George VI - 1¢ to 25¢, coins brilliant; leather mint case	$ 750.00
1937	George VI - 1¢ to 25¢, coins semi-brilliant; leather mint case	$ 550.00
1938	George VI - 1¢ to $1.00, coins brilliant.	$ 9,000.00
1944	George VI - 1¢, 5¢, 10¢, 25¢, 50¢ (only 2 known)	$ 4,000.00
1945	George VI - 1¢, 5¢, 10¢, 25¢, 50¢, $1.00.	$ 4,000.00
1946	George VI - 1¢, 5¢, 10¢, 25¢, 50¢, $1.00.	$ 4,000.00
1947	George VI - 1¢, 5¢, 10¢, 25¢, 50¢ (7 curved right), $1.00	$ 4,000.00
1947	George VI - 1¢, 5¢, 10¢, 25¢, 50¢ (7 curved left), $1.00	$ 4,000.00
1947 ML	George VI - 1¢, 5¢, 10¢, 25¢, 50¢ (7 curved left), $1.00	$ 4,500.00
1947 ML	George VI - 1¢, 5¢, 10¢, 25¢, 50¢ (7 curved right), $1.00	$ 7,000.00
1948	George VI - 1¢, 5¢, 10¢, 25¢, 50¢, $1.00.	$ 6,000.00
1949	George VI - 1¢, 5¢, 10¢, 25¢, 50¢, $1.00.	$ 1,500.00
1950	George VI - 1¢, 5¢, 10¢, 25¢, 50¢, $1.00.	$ 1,500.00
1951	George VI - 1¢, 5¢, 10¢, 25¢, 50¢, $1.00.	$ 1,500.00
1952	George VI - 1¢, 5¢, 10¢, 25¢, 50¢, $1.00 (water lines)	$ 1,500.00
1953	Elizabeth II - 1¢, 5¢, 10¢, 25¢, 50¢, $1.00 (no shoulder strap)	$ 1,200.00
1953	Elizabeth II - 1¢, 5¢, 10¢, 25¢, 50¢, $1.00 (shoulder strap)	$ 1,200.00
1964	Elizabeth II - 1¢, 5¢, 10¢, 25¢, 50¢, $1.00.	$ 300.00
1965	Elizabeth II - 1¢, 5¢, 10¢, 25¢, 50¢, $1.00.	$ 250.00
1970	Elizabeth II - 1¢, 5¢, 10¢, 25¢, 50¢, $1.00; black presentation case (V.I.P. issue 100)	$ 500.00
1971	Elizabeth II - 1¢, 5¢, 10¢, 25¢, 50¢, $1.00; black presentation case (V.I.P. issue 69)	$ 200.00
1972	Elizabeth II - 1¢, 5¢, 10¢, 25¢, 50¢, $1.00; black presentation case (V.I.P. issue 25)	$ 300.00
1973	Elizabeth II - 1¢, 5¢, 10¢, 25¢, 50¢, $1.00; black presentation case (V.I.P. issue 26)	$ 300.00
1974	Elizabeth II - 1¢, 5¢, 10¢, 25¢, 50¢, $1.00; black presentation case (V.I.P. issue 72)	$ 200.00
1975	Elizabeth II - 1¢, 5¢, 10¢, 25¢, 50¢, $1.00; black presentation case (V.I.P. issue 94)	$ 200.00

NOTE: Due to great rarity, some specimen sets seldom change hands, and this can result in wide price fluctuations between sales.

Specimen coins often sell at higher prices in sets than individually.

VICTORIA 1865 - 1896

Newfoundland's decimal coinage dates from 1865 when the large copper cents were issued. (Essais dated 1864 exist). The obverse depicts a draped laureate bust of Queen Victoria by L.C. Wyon and is similar to one used on the British Young Head halfpenny of the same period. The reverse consists of St. Edward's crown and date in a beaded circle surrounded by a wreath of pitcher plant. There are three varieties of the 1880 date: round 0, even date; round 0 low in date; and oval 0. The majority of the coins of Newfoundland were struck at the Tower Mint, London and have no mint mark. Those with the H mint mark of Heaton Mint, Birmingham, probably resulted from the Tower Mint sub-contracting with the private Heaton Mint during peak periods.

G-4 - Hair over ear worn through.
VG-8 - No details in the hair over ear.
F-12 - Strands of hair over ear begin to run together.
VF-20 - Hair and jewels no longer sharp but clear.
EF-40 - Hair over ear is sharp and clear. Jewels in diadem must show sharply and clearly.
AU-50 - Slight traces of wear on high points. Degree of mint lustre still present.
MS-60 - No traces of wear. High degree of lustre.

Designers: Obverse - L.C. Wyon.

Diameter: 25.527 mm; Weight: 5.670 grams; Composition: .950 copper, .040 tin, .010 zinc; Plain edge.

Date and Mint Mark	Quantity Minted	G-4	VG-8	F-12	VF-20	EF-40	AU-50	MS-60
1865	240,000	.75	1.50	2.50	5.00	10.00	30.00	50.00
1872H	200,000	.75	1.50	2.50	5.00	10.00	35.00	60.00
1873	200,025	.75	1.50	2.50	5.00	10.00	35.00	60.00
1876H	200,000	.75	1.50	2.50	5.00	10.00	35.00	60.00

Wide Round 0 Even Date	Wide Round 0 Low 0	Narrow Oval 0

Date and Mint Mark	Quantity Minted	G-4	VG-8	F-12	VF-20	EF-40	AU-50	MS-60
1880 Round 0, Even Date	400,000	.75	1.50	2.50	5.00	10.00	35.00	60.00
1880 Round 0, Low 0	Incl.	1.50	2.25	4.00	8.00	12.00	38.50	65.00
1880 Oval 0	Incl.	40.00	60.00	80.00	110.00	150.00	250.00	350.00
1885	40,000	12.50	20.00	25.00	30.00	40.00	82.50	125.00
1888	50,000	8.00	12.00	15.00	22.00	35.00	62.50	90.00
1890	200,000	.75	1.50	2.50	4.00	8.00	19.00	30.00
1894	200,000	.75	1.50	2.50	4.00	8.00	19.00	30.00
1896	200,000	.75	1.50	2.50	4.00	8.00	19.00	30.00

EDWARD VII 1904 - 1909

The obverse design depicts a crowned, robed bust of King Edward VII wearing the chain of the Order of the Garter fastened by a bow on the shoulder.

The Imperial State Crown replaces the St. Edward's Crown on the reverse. Otherwise, the reverse is similar to the Victoria issue.

Obverse Grading

G-4 - *Band of crown worn through*
VG-8 - *Band of crown worn through at the highest point.*
F-12 - *Jewels in the band of crown will be blurred.*
VF-20 - *Band of the crown is still clear but no longer sharp.*
EF-40 - *Band of crown slightly worn but generally sharp and clear including jewels.*
AU-50 - *Slight traces of wear on high points. Degree of mint lustre still present.*
MS-60 - *No traces of wear. High degree of lustre.*

Designer: Obverse - G.W. DeSaulles.

Diameter: 25.527 mm; Weight: 5.670 grams; Composition: .950 copper, .040 tin, .010 zinc; Plain edge.

Date and Mint Mark	Quantity Minted	G-4	VG-8	F-12	VF-20	EF-40	AU-50	MS-60
1904H	100,000	4.00	6.00	8.00	15.00	25.00	50.00	75.00
1907	200,000	1.00	1.50	3.00	6.00	12.00	31.00	50.00
1909	200,000	1.00	1.50	3.00	6.00	12.00	31.00	50.00

GEORGE V 1913 - 1936

The obverse portrait of King George V is the same as that used on the Canadian large cents of his reign.

The crowned King is wearing a robe with the chain of the Order of the Garter fastened by a bow at the shoulder. The reverse design is the same as the Edward VII issue.

Obverse Grading

G-4 - *Band of crown worn through*
VG-8 - *Band of crown worn through at the highest point.*
F-12 - *Jewels in the band of crown will be blurred.*
VF-20 - *Band of crown is still clear but no longer sharp.*
EF-40 - *Band of crown slightly worn but generally sharp and clear including jewels.*
AU-50 - *Slight traces of wear on high points. Degree of mint lustre still present.*
MS-60 - *No traces of wear. High degree of lustre.*

Designer: Obverse - Sir E.B. MacKennal.

Diameter: 1913, 1929, 1936 - 25.527 mm; 1917-1920 - 25.40 mm; Weight: 5.670 grams; Composition: 1913-1920 - .950 copper, .040 tin, .010 zinc; 1929-1936 - .955 copper, .030 tin, .015 zinc; Plain edge.

Date and Mint Mark	Quantity Minted	G-4	VG-8	F-12	VF-20	EF-40	AU-50	MS-60
1913	400,000	.40	.75	1.00	2.00	4.00	14.50	25.00
1917C	702,350	.40	.75	1.00	2.00	4.00	14.50	25.00
1919C	300,000	.40	.75	1.00	2.00	4.00	14.50	25.00
1920C	302,184	.40	.75	1.00	2.00	4.00	14.50	25.00
1929	300,000	.40	.75	1.00	2.00	4.00	14.50	25.00
1936	300,000	.40	.75	1.00	2.00	4.00	12.00	20.00

SMALL CENTS
GEORGE VI 1938 - 1947

A change was made from the large to small cent, with the George VI issue, for economy and convenience. The obverse portrait of the crowned King was by Percy Metcalfe and his initials P.M. are below the neck.

The reverse design depicts the pitcher plant in bloom. This plant is native to Newfoundland and is one of the carnivores of the vegetable kingdom. The green leaves are pitcher-like receptacles, the inner surfaces being covered with downward sloping bristles which prevent the escape of any insect which may have entered to feed on the sweet sticky syrup at the bottom of the pitcher. The digestable portions of the insect are then absorbed by the plant.

Apart from the 1938 issue which was struck at the Tower Mint, all of the small cents were produced at the Royal Canadian Mint, due to World War II shipping hazards. The C mint mark was omitted in error in 1940 and 1942.

G-4   - Band of crown worn through.
VG-8   - Band of the crown is worn through at the highest point.
F-12   - Jewels in the band of crown will be blurred.
VF-20   - Band of the crown is still clear but no longer sharp.
EF-40   - Band of the crown slightly worn but generally sharp and clear, including jewels.
AU-50   - Slight traces of wear on high points. Degree of mint lustre still present.
MS-60   - No traces of wear. High degree of lustre.

Designer: Obverse - Percy Metcalfe.

Diameter: 19.050 mm; Weight: 3.240 grams; Composition: .955 copper, .030 tin, .015 zinc; Plain edge.

Date and Mint Mark	Quantity Minted	VG-8	F-12	VF-20	EF-40	AU-50	MS-60
1938	500,000	.60	.75	1.50	2.50	7.25	12.00
1940	300,000	2.50	3.50	5.50	9.00	17.00	25.00
1940 Re-engraved Date		12.00	15.00	25.00	30.00	40.00	50.00
1941C	827,662	.30	.50	.75	1.25	4.25	7.00
1942	1,996,889	.30	.50	.75	1.25	4.25	7.00
1943C	1,239,732	.30	.50	.75	1.25	4.25	7.00
1944C	1,328,776	1.50	2.50	3.00	4.50	12.50	20.00
1947C	313,772	.75	1.00	1.75	3.00	7.50	12.00

5 CENTS
VICTORIA 1865 - 1896

Obverse portrait of Queen Victoria by L.C. Wyon is similar to the one used on Canadian and New Brunswick 5 cent coins of her reign. The reverse design has value and date in a beaded circle surrounded by a continuous ornamental frame.

Unimportant differences in the Queen's facial features and periods present, or missing, before and after Newfoundland, are known, but are of no significance to most collectors.

G-4   - Braid worn through near ear.
VG-8   - No detail in braid around ear.
F-12   - Segments of braid begin to merge into one another.
VF-20   - Braid is clear but not sharp.
EF-40   - Braid is slightly worn but generally sharp and clear.
AU-50   - Slight traces of wear on high points. Degree of mint lustre still present.
MS-60   - No traces of wear. High degree of lustre.

Designer: Obverse - L.C. Wyon.

Diameter: 15.500 mm; Weight: 1.178 grams; Composition: .925 silver, .075 copper; Reeded edge.

A rare variety of the 1873 date struck at the Heaton Mint has the H mint mark below the Queen's neck.

Date and Mint Mark	Quantity Minted	G-4	VG-8	F-12	VF-20	EF-40	AU-50	MS-60
1865	80,000	15.00	30.00	40.00	80.00	200.00	275.00	350.00
1870	40,000	15.00	30.00	40.00	80.00	225.00	300.00	375.00
1872H	40,000	13.00	25.00	35.00	70.00	225.00	300.00	375.00
1873	44,260	15.00	30.00	40.00	80.00	225.00	300.00	375.00
1873H	Incl.	200.00	400.00	600.00	1,200.00	2,000.00	2,225.00	2,500.00
1876H	20,000	25.00	45.00	55.00	150.00	500.00	750.00	1,000.00
1880	40,000	19.00	25.00	40.00	90.00	250.00	312.50	375.00
1881	40,000	13.00	20.00	30.00	60.00	160.00	230.00	300.00
1882H	60,000	12.00	18.00	30.00	60.00	160.00	230.00	300.00
1885	16,000	60.00	80.00	100.00	225.00	600.00	725.00	850.00
1888	40,000	12.00	18.00	30.00	60.00	175.00	237.50	300.00
1890	160,000	5.00	10.00	20.00	50.00	150.00	200.00	250.00
1894	160,000	5.00	10.00	20.00	50.00	150.00	200.00	250.00
1896	400,000	4.00	8.00	15.00	40.00	140.00	190.00	240.00

EDWARD VII 1903 - 1908

The obverse portrait by G.W. DeSaulles (DES below bust) is the same as used on Canadian silver coins. He also designed the reverse, consisting of a circle opening into an ornamental design at the bottom.

G-4	- Band of crown worn through.
VG-8	- Band of crown worn through at the highest point.
F-12	- Jewels in the band of crown will be blurred.
VF-20	- Band of the crown is still clear but no longer sharp.
EF-40	- Band of crown slightly worn but generally sharp and clear, including jewels.
AU-50	- Slight traces of wear on high points. Degree of mint lustre still present.
MS-60	- No traces of wear. High degree of lustre.

Designer: Obverse & Reverse - G.W. DeSaulles.

Diameter: 15.500 mm; Weight: 1.178 grams; Composition: .925 silver, .075 copper; Reeded edge.

Date and Mint Mark	Quantity Minted	G-4	VG-8	F-12	VF-20	EF-40	AU-50	MS-60
1903	100,000	1.50	3.00	6.00	15.00	35.00	130.00	225.00
1904H	100,000	1.50	3.00	6.00	12.00	30.00	115.00	200.00
1908	400,000	1.25	2.50	5.00	10.00	25.00	75.00	125.00

GEORGE V 1912 - 1929

The obverse portrait of King George V is the same as used on Canadian 5 cent coins. Designer's initials B.M. at base of bust. The reverse design of Edward VII issue was retained.

G-4	- Band of crown worn through.
VG-8	- Band of crown worn through at the highest point.
F-12	- Jewels in the band of crown will be blurred.
VF-20	- Band of crown is still clear but no longer sharp.
EF-40	- Band of crown slightly worn but generally sharp and clear, including jewels.
AU-50	- Slight traces of wear on high points. Degree of mint lustre still present.
MS-60	- No traces of wear. High degree of lustre.

Designers: Obverse - Sir E.B. MacKennal; Reverse - G.W. DeSaulles.

Diameter: 1912-1919C - 15.500 mm; 1929 - 15.700 mm; Weight: 1912 - 1.178 grams; 1917C-1929 - 1.166 grams; Composition: .925 silver, .075 copper; Reeded edge.

5 CENTS
GEORGE V 1912 - 1929

Date and Mint Mark	Quantity Minted	G-4	VG-8	F-12	VF-20	EF-40	AU-50	MS-60
1912	300,000	.75	1.50	3.00	6.00	15.00	70.00	125.00
1917C	300,319	.75	1.50	3.00	6.00	15.00	62.50	110.00
1919C	100,844	1.75	3.00	5.00	8.00	20.00	72.50	125.00
1929	300,000	.65	1.00	2.00	4.00	10.00	55.00	100.00

GEORGE VI 1938 - 1947

The obverse portrait of King George VI by Percy Metcalfe differs from that used on Canadian coins. Designer's initials P.M. are below neck. The previous reverse design was continued.

G-4 — Band of crown worn through.
VG-8 — Band of the crown is worn through at the highest point.
F-12 — Jewels in the band of crown will be blurred.
VF-20 — Band of the crown is still clear but no longer sharp.
EF-40 — Band of the crown slightly worn but generally sharp and clear, including jewels.
AU-50 — Slight traces of wear on high points. Degree of mint lustre still present.
MS-60 — No traces of wear. High degree of lustre.

Designers: Obverse - Percy Metcalfe; Reverse - G.W. DeSaulles.

Diameter: 1938 - 15.700 mm; 1940-1947 - 15.500 mm; Weight: 1.166 grams; Composition: 1938-1944 - .925 silver, .075 copper; 1945-1947 - .800 silver, .200 copper; Reeded edge.

Due to the very small minting, the 1946C is scarce and valuable.

Date and Mint Mark	Quantity Minted	VG-8	F-12	VF-20	EF-40	AU-50	MS-60
1938	100,000	.65	1.00	2.50	5.50	27.75	50.00
1940C	200,000	.50	.75	1.75	3.50	14.25	25.00
1941C	612,641	.45	.65	1.00	2.00	11.00	20.00
1942C	298,348	1.50	2.00	2.50	4.00	14.50	25.00
1943C	351,666	.40	.60	.75	1.50	10.75	20.00
1944C	286,504	.75	1.25	1.75	3.50	16.75	30.00
1945C	203,828	.40	.60	.75	1.50	10.75	20.00
1946C	2,041	125.00	150.00	175.00	300.00	450.00	600.00
1947C	38,400	4.00	6.00	8.00	11.00	30.50	50.00

10 CENTS

VICTORIA 1865 - 1896

The obverse portrait of Queen Victoria is similar to that used on Canadian and New Brunswick 10 cent coins. The reverse design is the same as on the Newfoundland 5 cents of Victoria. The second 8 in 1880 has the 8 punched over a 7.

Some unimportant differences occur in the Queen's facial features and a period present or missing after Newfoudnalnd. No change in value results from such variants.

G-4 — Braid worn through near ear.
VG-8 — No detail in braid around ear.
F-12 — Segments of braid begin to merge into one another.
VF-20 — Braid is clear but not sharp.
EF-40 — Braid is slightly worn but generally sharp and clear.
AU-50 — Slight traces of wear on high points. Degree of mint lustre still present.
MS-60 — No traces of wear. High degree of lustre.

Designers: Obverse & Reverse - L.C. Wyon.

Diameter: 18.000 mm; Weight: 2.356 grams; Composition: .925 silver, .075 copper; Reeded edge.

Second 8 In Date Punched Over 7

A rare variety of a 10 cent coin exists with a Newfoundland obverse and a Canadian reverse dated 1871H.

Date and Mint Mark	Quantity Minted	G-4	VG-8	F-12	VF-20	EF-40	AU-50	MS-60
1865	80,000	8.00	15.00	25.00	45.00	90.00	295.00	500.00
1870	30,000	75.00	125.00	200.00	300.00	500.00	850.00	1,200.00
1872H	40,000	7.00	12.00	20.00	35.00	70.00	285.00	500.00
1873	23,614	12.00	20.00	30.00	45.00	90.00	345.00	600.00
1876H	10,000	15.00	25.00	45.00	90.00	180.00	490.00	800.00
1880	10,000	15.00	25.00	45.00	90.00	180.00	440.00	700.00
1882H	20,000	7.00	12.00	20.00	35.00	70.00	285.00	500.00
1885	8,000	25.00	50.00	75.00	150.00	250.00	575.00	900.00
1888	30,000	8.00	15.00	20.00	35.00	70.00	210.00	350.00
1890	100,000	3.00	6.00	12.00	25.00	50.00	175.00	300.00
1894	100,000	3.00	6.00	12.00	25.00	50.00	175.00	300.00
1896	230,000	2.50	5.00	10.00	25.00	50.00	175.00	300.00

EDWARD VII 1903 - 1904

The obverse portrait by G.W. DeSaulles, (DES below bust), is the same as used on the Canadian 10 cent coins. The reverse design is similar to that of the Newfoundland 5 cents of Edward VII.

G-4	- Band of crown worn through.
VG-8	- Band of crown worn through at the highest point.
F-12	- Jewels in the band of crown will be blurred.
VF-20	- Band of the crown is still clear but no longer sharp.
EF-40	- Band of crown slightly worn but generally sharp and clear, including jewels.
AU-50	- Slight traces of wear on high points. Degree of mint lustre still present.
MS-60	- No traces of wear. High degree of lustre.

Designer: Obverse & Reverse - G.W. DeSaulles.

Diameter: 18.000 mm; Weight: 2.356 grams; Composition: .925 silver, .075 copper; Reeded edge.

Date and Mint Mark	Quantity Minted	G-4	VG-8	F-12	VF-20	EF-40	AU-50	MS-60
1903	100,000	2.00	4.00	8.00	20.00	45.00	122.50	200.00
1904H	100,000	2.00	4.00	8.00	20.00	45.00	122.50	200.00

GEORGE V 1912 - 1919

The obverse portrait is the same as used on the Canadian issue. Designer's initials B.M. at base of bust. The reverse is unchanged from Edward VII series.

G-4	- Band of crown worn through.
VG-8	- Band of crown worn through at the highest point.
F-12	- Jewels in the band of crown will be blurred.
VF-20	- Band of crown is still clear but no longer sharp.
EF-40	- Band of crown slightly worn but generally sharp and clear, including jewels.
AU-50	- Slight traces of wear on high points. Degree of mint lustre still present.
MS-60	- No traces of wear. High degree of lustre.

Designer: Obverse - Sir E.B. MacKennal.

Diameter: 1912 - 18.000 mm; 1917, 1919 - 18.034 mm; Weight: 1912 - 2.356 grams; 1917, 1919 - 2.333 grams; Composition: .925 silver, .075 copper; Reeded edge.

Date and Mint Mark	Quantity Minted	G-4	VG-8	F-12	VF-20	EF-40	AU-50	MS-60
1912	150,000	1.50	3.00	6.00	12.00	25.00	87.50	150.00
1917C	250,805	1.25	2.50	5.00	10.00	20.00	60.00	100.00
1919C	54,342	2.00	3.50	7.00	15.00	30.00	55.00	80.00

GEORGE VI 1938 - 1947

The obverse portrait is the same as used on the Newfoundland 5 cent coin of George VI. Designer's initials P.M. below neck. Reverse design unchanged from Edward VII and George V issues.

G-4 - Band of crown worn through.
VG-8 - Band of the crown is worn through at the highest point.
F-12 - Jewels in the band of crown will be blurred.
VF-20 - Band of the crown is still clear but no longer sharp.
EF-40 - Band of the crown slightly worn but generally sharp and clear, including jewels.
AU-50 - Slight traces of wear on high points. Degree of mint lustre still present.
MS-60 - No traces of wear. High degree of lustre.

Designers: Obverse - Percy Metcalfe; Reverse - G.W. DeSaulles.

Diameter: 18.034 mm; Weight: 2.333 grams; Composition: 1938-1944 - .925 silver, .075 copper; 1945-1947 - .800 silver, .200 copper; Reeded edge.

Date and Mint Mark	Quantity Minted	VG-8	F-12	VF-20	EF-40	AU-50	MS-60
1938	100,000	.75	1.50	3.00	6.00	18.00	30.00
1940	100,000	.75	1.25	2.50	5.00	15.00	25.00
1941C	483,630	.50	.75	1.50	3.00	11.50	20.00
1942C	292,736	.50	.75	1.50	3.00	11.50	20.00
1943C	104,706	.50	.75	1.50	3.00	11.50	20.00
1944C	151,471	.70	1.15	2.50	5.00	15.00	25.00
1945C	175,833	.50	.75	1.25	3.00	11.50	20.00
1946C	38,400	5.00	7.00	8.50	10.00	47.50	85.00
1947C	61,988	2.50	3.50	5.00	7.00	16.00	25.00

20 CENTS
VICTORIA 1865 - 1900

The obverse portrait of Queen Victoria is the same as used on the Canadian and New Brunswick 20 cent pieces.
Some unimportant changes in facial features and the use of Roman and Arabic numerals are of no significance to most collectors.
The reverse design is the same as used on the Newfoundland 5 and 10 cent issues of Victoria.

G-4 - Braid worn through near ear.
VG-8 - No detail in braid around ear.
F-12 - Segments of braid begin to merge into one another.
VF-20 - Braid is clear but not sharp.
EF-40 - Braid is slightly worn but generally sharp and clear.
AU-50 - Slight traces of wear on high points. Degree of mint lustre still present.
MS-60 - No traces of wear. High degree of lustre.

Designer: Obverse & Reverse - L.C. Wyon.

Diameter: 23.190 mm; Weight: 4.713 grams; Composition: .925 silver, .075 copper; Reeded edge.

Narrow Date
(Small 96)

Wide Date
(Large 96)

Large 99

Small 99

There are two varieties of the 1896 and 1899 issues, distinguished by the size of the last two figures in each date.

Date and Mint Mark	Quantity Minted	G-4	VG-8	F-12	VF-20	EF-40	AU-50	MS-60
1865	100,000	4.00	8.00	15.00	40.00	90.00	345.00	600.00
1870	50,000	6.00	12.00	25.00	50.00	100.00	400.00	700.00
1872H	90,000	3.50	6.00	12.00	40.00	75.00	337.50	600.00
1873	45,797	4.00	8.00	15.00	45.00	95.00	372.50	650.00
1876H	50,000	6.00	12.00	20.00	50.00	125.00	462.50	800.00
1880	30,000	6.00	10.00	20.00	50.00	125.00	462.50	800.00
1881	60,000	2.50	4.00	9.00	35.00	75.00	312.50	550.00
1882H	100,000	1.50	3.00	8.00	30.00	70.00	285.00	500.00
1885	40,000	1.50	3.00	8.00	30.00	70.00	285.00	500.00
1888	75,000	1.50	2.50	5.00	20.00	50.00	250.00	450.00
1890	100,000	1.25	2.50	5.00	15.00	40.00	232.50	425.00
1894	100,000	1.25	2.50	5.00	15.00	40.00	232.50	425.00
1896 Small 96	125,000	1.25	2.50	5.00	15.00	40.00	232.50	425.00
1896 Large 96	Incl.	2.50	4.50	9.00	25.00	50.00	262.50	475.00
1899 Large 99	125,000	1.25	2.50	5.00	15.00	40.00	220.00	400.00
1899 Small 99	Incl.	3.00	4.50	9.00	25.00	45.00	222.50	400.00
1900	125,000	1.25	2.25	4.50	12.00	35.00	205.00	375.00

EDWARD VII 1904

The obverse portrait by G.W. DeSaulles (DES below bust) is similar to that on the Canadian 25 cent coin denominations. The reverse design was copied and engraved by W.H.J. Blakemore from a similar design of G.W. DeSaulles, on the 5 and 10 cent denominations. This single year issue is scarce.

G-4	- Band of crown worn through.
VG-8	- Band of crown worn through at the highest point.
F-12	- Jewels in the band of crown will be blurred.
VF-20	- Band of the crown is still clear but no longer sharp.
EF-40	- Band of crown slightly worn but generally sharp and clear, including jewels.
AU-50	- Slight traces of wear on high points. Degree of mint lustre still present.
MS-60	- No traces of wear. High degree of lustre.

Designers: Obverse - G.W. DeSaulles; Reverse - W.H.J. Blakemore.

Diameter: 23.190 mm; Weight: 4.713 grams; Composition: .925 silver, .075 copper; Reeded edge.

Date and Mint Mark	Quantity Minted	G-4	VG-8	F-12	VF-20	EF-40	AU-50	MS-60
1904H	75,000	4.50	8.00	15.00	50.00	100.00	400.00	700.00

GEORGE V 1912

The obverse portrait by Sir E.B. MacKennal (B.M. at base of bust). The reverse design was the same as used on the 1904 issue.
This is by far the largest issue of the 20 cent piece and is the most common.

G-4	- Band of crown worn through.
VG-8	- Band of crown worn through at the highest point.
F-12	- Jewels in the band of crown will be blurred.
VF-20	- Band of crown is still clear but no longer sharp.
EF-40	- Band of crown slightly worn but generally sharp and clear, including jewels.
AU-50	- Slight traces of wear on high points. Degree of mint lustre still present.
MS-60	- No traces of wear. High degree of lustre.

Designer: Obverse - Sir E.B. MacKennal; Reverse - W.H.J. Blakemore.

Diameter: 23.190 mm; Weight: 4.713 grams; Composition: .925 silver, .075 copper; Reeded edge.

Date and Mint Mark	Quantity Minted	G-4	VG-8	F-12	VF-20	EF-40	AU-50	MS-60
1912	350,000	1.00	2.00	4.00	15.00	30.00	165.00	300.00

25 CENTS

GEORGE V 1917 - 1919

The obverse portrait is the same as used on the Canadian 25 cent denomination. Designer's initials B.M. below bust. The reverse design is similar to the 20 cent issue. Confusion between the Newfoundland 20 cent coin and the Canadian 25 cent piece led to Newfoundland making a change to the 25 cent denomination.

G-4	- Band of crown worn through.
VG-8	- Band of the crown is worn through at the highest point.
F-12	- Jewels in the band of crown will be blurred.
VF-20	- Band of the crown is still clear but no longer sharp.
EF-40	- Band of the crown slightly worn but generally sharp and clear, including jewels.
AU-50	- Slight traces of wear on high points. Degree of mint lustre still present.
MS-60	- No traces of wear. High degree of lustre.

Designers: Obverse - Sir E.B. MacKennal; Reverse - W.H.J. Blakemore.

Diameter: 23.622 mm; Weight: 5.832 grams; Composition: .925 silver, .075 copper; Reeded edge.

Date and Mint Mark	Quantity Minted	VG-8	F-12	VF-20	EF-40	AU-50	MS-60
1917C	464,779	1.50	2.25	3.50	7.00	28.50	50.00
1919C	163,939	1.50	2.50	4.50	8.00	34.00	60.00

VICTORIA 1870 - 1900

The laureate portrait of Queen Victoria and the ornamental reverse were designed and engraved by L.C. Wyon. The second 8 in date of 1880 is punched over a 7.

Facial features show some variations but these are of no significance to most collectors.

G-4	- Braid worn through near ear.
VG-8	- No detail in braid around ear.
F-12	- Segments of braid begin to merge into one another.
VF-20	- Braid is clear but not sharp.
EF-40	- Braid is slightly worn but generally sharp and clear.
AU-50	- Slight traces of wear on high points. Degree of mint lustre still present.
MS-60	- No traces of wear. High degree of lustre.

Designers: Obverse & Reverse - L.C. Wyon.

Diameter: 29.845 mm; Weight: 11.782 grams; Composition: .925 silver, .075 copper; Reeded edge.

Second 8 In Date Punched Over 7

Small Date

Large Date

Narrow 9's

Wide 9's

There are small and large date 1896's. The 1899 was issued with both narrow and wide 9's.

Date and Mint Mark	Quantity Minted	G-4	VG-8	F-12	VF-20	EF-40	AU-50	MS-60
1870	50,000	4.00	8.00	15.00	35.00	100.00	500.00	900.00
1872H	48,000	4.00	8.00	15.00	35.00	100.00	500.00	900.00
1873	37,675	4.00	8.00	15.00	35.00	100.00	500.00	900.00
1874	80,000	4.00	8.00	15.00	35.00	100.00	500.00	900.00
1876H	28,000	7.50	15.00	25.00	75.00	200.00	850.00	1,500.00
1880	24,000	7.50	15.00	25.00	65.00	175.00	687.50	1,200.00
1881	50,000	4.00	8.00	15.00	40.00	100.00	500.00	900.00
1882H	100,000	3.50	7.00	10.00	30.00	90.00	495.00	900.00
1885	40,000	6.00	12.00	20.00	50.00	150.00	675.00	1,200.00
1888	20,000	7.50	15.00	25.00	60.00	175.00	837.50	1,500.00
1894	40,000	2.75	4.00	8.00	30.00	75.00	437.50	800.00
1896 Small Date	60,000	2.50	3.00	6.00	25.00	70.00	435.00	800.00
1896 Large Date	Incl.	2.50	3.00	6.00	25.00	70.00	435.00	800.00
1898	79,607	2.50	3.00	5.50	25.00	70.00	435.00	800.00
1899 Narrow 9's	150,000	2.50	3.00	5.50	25.00	70.00	435.00	800.00
1899 Wide 9's	Incl.	2.50	3.00	5.50	25.00	70.00	435.00	800.00
1900	150,000	2.50	3.00	5.00	20.00	60.00	405.00	750.00

EDWARD VII 1904 - 1909

The obverse bust designed and engraved by G.W. DeSaulles (DES below bust), is the same as used on Canadian coins.
The reverse design by W.H.J. Blakemore was copied from a similar one of DeSaulles, used on the 5 and 10 cent denominations.

G-4	- Band of crown worn through.
VG-8	- Band of crown worn through at the highest point.
F-12	- Jewels in the band of crown will be blurred.
VF-20	- Band of the crown is still clear but no longer sharp.
EF-40	- Band of crown slightly worn but generally sharp and clear, including jewels.
AU-50	- Slight traces of wear on high points. Degree of mint lustre still present.
MS-60	- No traces of wear. High degree of lustre.

Designers: Obverse - G.W. DeSaulles; Reverse - W.H.J. Blakemore.

Diameter: 29.845 mm; Weight: 11.782 grams; Composition: .975 silver, .075 copper; Reeded edge.

Date and Mint Mark	Quantity Minted	G-4	VG-8	F-12	VF-20	EF-40	AU-50	MS-60
1904H	140,000	2.50	3.00	5.00	20.00	45.00	160.00	275.00
1907	100,000	2.50	3.00	5.00	20.00	45.00	160.00	275.00
1908	160,000	2.50	3.00	5.00	17.50	35.00	130.00	225.00
1909	200,000	2.50	3.00	5.00	17.50	35.00	130.00	225.00

GEORGE V 1911 - 1919

The obverse bust designed by Sir E.B. MacKennal (B.M. at base of bust) is the same as that used on the Canadian issues.
No change in reverse design of Edward VII.

G-4	- Band of crown worn through.
VG-8	- Band of crown worn through at the highest point.
F-12	- Jewels in the band of crown will be blurred.
VF-20	- Band of crown is still clear but no longer sharp.
EF-40	- Band of crown slightly worn but generally sharp and clear, including jewels.
AU-50	- Slight traces of wear on high points. Degree of mint lustre still present.
MS-60	- No traces of wear. High degree of lustre.

Designers: Obverse - Sir E.B. MacKennal; Reverse - W.H.J. Blakemore.

Diameter: 1911 - 29.845 mm; 1917-1919 - 29.718 mm; Weight: 1911 - 11.782 grams; 1917-1919 - 11.664 grams; Composition: .925 silver, .075 copper; Reeded edge.

Date and Mint Mark	Quantity Minted	G-4	VG-8	F-12	VF-20	EF-40	AU-50	MS-60
1911	200,000	2.50	3.25	5.50	12.00	25.00	75.00	125.00
1917C	375,560	2.50	3.00	4.25	8.50	20.00	60.00	100.00
1918C	294,824	2.50	3.00	4.25	8.50	20.00	60.00	100.00
1919C	306,267	2.50	3.00	4.25	8.50	20.00	60.00	100.00

VICTORIA 1865 - 1888

The obverse and reverse designed and engraved by L.C. Wyon. A most unusual feature of this coin is the denomination in dollars, pence and cents.
The diameter and portrait are the same as for the Canadian 10 cent coin.

G-4 - Braid worn through near ear.
VG-8 - No detail in braid around ear.
F-12 - Segments of braid begin to merge into one another.
VF-20 - Braid is clear but not sharp.
EF-40 - Braid is slightly worn but generally sharp and clear.
AU-50 - Slight traces of wear on high points. Degree of mint lustre still present.
MS-60 - No traces of wear. High degree of lustre.

Designer: Obverse & Reverse - L.C. Wyon.

Diameter: 18.000 mm; Weight: 3.328 grams; Composition: .917 gold, .083 copper; Reeded edge.

Date and Mint Mark	Quantity Minted	F-12	VF-20	EF-40	AU-50	MS-60
1865	10,000	125.00	175.00	225.00	362.50	500.00
1870	10,000	125.00	175.00	225.00	362.50	500.00
1872	6,050	225.00	300.00	400.00	575.00	750.00
1880	2,500	650.00	1,000.00	1,200.00	1,600.00	2,000.00
1881	10,000	110.00	160.00	185.00	242.50	300.00
1882H	25,000	100.00	150.00	175.00	237.50	300.00
1885	10,000	110.00	160.00	185.00	242.50	300.00
1888	25,000	100.00	150.00	175.00	237.50	300.00

DECIMAL COINS OF THE ATLANTIC PROVINCES

The decimal coins of Prince Edward Island, Nova Scotia and New Brunswick have always been listed among the older tokens of the Colonial period. It is thought that a separate listing for these coins would make it easier for collectors to find the listings, as well as emphasize their true status as regal coins distinct from the semi-regal and private tokens of earlier times.

PRINCE EDWARD ISLAND

Prince Edward Island adopted the decimal system in 1871, based on a dollar equal in value to the Canadian dollar. The only coinage was an issue of two million cents in 1871. The cent was coined in bronze at 80 to the pound avoirdupois, or 87.5 grains, and is an inch in diameter. It is the only coin issued in British North America with the Royal Titles in English and the only coin of the Heaton Mint for any part of Canada without the letter H mint mark. The obverse was engraved by L.C. Wyon from a bust of William Theed. The reverse was engraved by L.C. Wyon from the seal of the island.

Diameter: 25.400 mm; Weight: 5.670 grams.

Date	G-4	VG-8	F-12	VF-20	EF-40	AU-50	MS-60
1871 Cent	.65	1.25	2.50	5.50	11.00	35.00	60.00

NOVA SCOTIA

Nova Scotia adopted the decimal system in 1859, based on a dollar such that five dollars equalled a pound sterling. This enabled Nova Scotia to continue using British silver and thus avoid the expense of a domestic silver coinage. The first decimal coins were cents and half-cents which appeared late in 1861. There was an issue of cents in 1862 and a further issue of cents and half-cents in 1864. The coins were struck at the Royal Mint in bronze. The obverse dies were designed and engraved by L.C. Wyon. The reverse die was designed by C. Hill and engraved by Wyon. The cent weights 87.5 grains and the half-cent 43.75 grains. There are two varieties of the 1861 cent, differing in the size of the rosebud to the right of the word SCOTIA.

Half-cent - Diameter: 20.650 mm; Weight: 2.835 grams.
Cent - Diameter: 25.527 mm; Weight: 5.670 grams.

Date and Mint Mark	Quantity Minted	G-4	VG-8	F-12	VF-20	EF-40	AU-50	MS-60
1861 Half Cent	400,000	3.50	6.00	8.00	10.00	14.00	19.50	25.00
1864 Half Cent	400,000	3.50	6.00	8.00	10.00	14.00	19.50	25.00
1861 Cent, large rosebud	800,000	1.25	2.50	5.00	7.50	15.00	22.50	30.00
1861 Cent, small rosebud	Incl.	.75	1.50	2.50	5.00	10.00	17.50	25.00
*1862 Cent	1,000,000	9.00	15.00	22.00	40.00	55.00	102.50	150.00
1864 Cent	800,000	.80	1.60	2.75	6.00	10.00	17.50	25.00

*The scarcity of the 1862 Cent is due to the fact that most of the cents issued in 1862 were dated 1861.

DECIMAL COINS OF THE ATLANTIC PROVINCES

Nova Scotia's currency differed from the Canadian even after Confederation, until 1871, when a uniform currency was established in the Dominion as it extended then. Nova Scotia currency was thus superseded by Canadian, all accounts, debts, and financial matters being converted at the rate of 73 cents in Canadian currency for 75 cents in Nova Scotian currency.

NEW BRUNSWICK

New Brunswick adopted the decimal system in 1860, choosing a dollar equal in value to the Canadian dollar. The first coins were bronze cents issued in 1861. The half-cent of 1861 was coined in the mistaken belief that New Brunswick's currency was on the same standard as Nova Scotia's. It is believed that 222,800 pieces were struck before the mistake was realized. Although most of these were melted, some were apparently inadvertently mixed with a shipment of half-cents for Nova Scotia, and put into circulation there. A further issue of cents was released in 1864. The cent and half-cent were coined in bronze, the cent weighing 87.5 grains and the half-cent 43.75 grains. The obverses were designed and engraved by L.C. Wyon, while the reverses were designed by C. Hill and engraved by L.C. Wyon.

Silver coins in denominations of five, ten and twenty cents were issued in 1862 and 1864. The coins were designed and engraved by L.C. Wyon, though this is not certain as regards the twenty cent piece. The reverse of this coin may have been the work of George W. Wyon. The silver coinage was struck in sterling silver. The weights of the five, ten and twenty cent pieces are respectively: 17.93 grains (1.162 grams), 35.86 grains (2.324 grams), and 71.73 grains (4.648 grams).

Date and Mint Mark	Quantity Minted	G-4	VG-8	F-12	VF-20	EF-40	AU-50	MS-60
1861 Half Cent	222,800	25.00	40.00	50.00	60.00	75.00	125.00	175.00
1861 Cent	1,000,000	.75	1.50	2.50	5.00	10.00	17.50	25.00
1864 Cent	1,000,000	.75	1.50	2.50	5.00	10.00	17.50	25.00
1862 Five Cents	100,000	20.00	28.00	40.00	60.00	80.00	215.00	350.00
1864 Five Cents	100,000	20.00	28.00	40.00	55.00	80.00	210.00	340.00
1862 Ten Cents	150,000	15.00	22.00	32.00	50.00	100.00	212.50	325.00
1862 Ten Cents, double-punched 2		14.00	20.00	30.00	45.00	90.00	195.00	300.00
1864 Ten Cents	100,000	14.00	20.00	30.00	50.00	100.00	300.00	500.00
1862 Twenty Cents	150,000	7.00	12.00	18.00	25.00	40.00	157.50	275.00
1864 Twenty Cents	150,000	8.00	13.00	20.00	28.00	45.00	165.00	285.00

PATTERNS, TRIAL PIECES AND OFFICIAL CONCOCTIONS

A *PATTERN* is a piece submitted as a design sample by engravers when a new coinage is contemplated. If the design is adopted for regular coinage with the same date, the piece ceases to be a pattern. If the design is adopted with a later date, the piece remains a pattern. Patterns are usually struck as proofs.

A *TRIAL PIECE* or *ESSAI* is from dies already accepted for regular coinage. It may bear a date or mint mark other than on the coins issued for circulation or it may be in a different metal.

The *OFFICIAL CONCOCTION* is a piece that was created for some special purpose unconnected with design proposals or experiments on coinage design or metals. For example, the New Brunswick pieces bearing the dates 1870, 1871 and 1875 were obviously not connected with an attempt to revive a separate coinage for that province after confederation.

The best listing of patterns, trial pieces and official concoctions has been by Fred Bowman in his book "Canadian Patterns". The present listing is greatly revised compared to Bowman's and new numbers are used. However, Bowman's original numbers are also included for those pieces which were listed in his book.

The most complete collection of this kind of material is in the National Currency Collection at the Bank of Canada in Ottawa. We wish to express special thanks to the curators of that collection for their co-operation in allowing us to examine the collection, for providing many of the photographs used in this section, and for many helpful suggestions regarding the manuscript and the existence of numerous previously unpublished pieces.

PROVINCE OF CANADA

PATTERNS

BOWMAN NUMBERS	CHARLTON NUMBERS	
B-4	PC-1	One Cent 1858, bronze. Uniface - obverse blank. Not a proof. Reverse - wreath of maple leaves and seed pods with beaded circle containing ONE/CENT/1858. (National Currency Collection)

B-4	PC-2	One Cent 1858, bronze. Uniface - obverse blank. Proof. Reverse - similar to PC-1 except the date is more closely spaced and the device is farther from the inner beaded circle. (National Currency Collection)

B-3	PC-3	One Cent 1858, bronze. Proof. Obverse - adopted legend with diademed bust of Victoria. Reverse - pattern design as on PC-2. (Wayte Raymond Sale 1928)

B-6	PC-4	Twenty-Cents 1858, silver. Plain edge proof, dies ↑↑. Obverse - adopted design. Reverse - adopted design for New Brunswick. (National Currency Collection)

PROVINCE OF CANADA

BOWMAN NUMBERS	CHARLTON NUMBERS	
B-5	PC-5	One Cent 1859 (in Roman numerals), bronze. Proof. Obverse - adopted design. Reverse - Britannia reverse for a pattern British halfpenny. (Parsons Collection 1936)

TRIAL PIECES

	PC-6	One Cent 1858, cupro-nickel. Dies ↑↑. Adopted design; struck from proof dies on an unpolished blank of double thickness. (National Currency Collection)
	PC-7	One Cent 1858, cupro-nickel. Proof; dies ↑↑. Adopted design; normal thickness. (National Currency Collection)

NOVA SCOTIA

PATTERNS

B-14	NS-1	Half Cent 186 - , bronze. Proof. Obverse - adopted (small bust) design by L.C. Wyon. Reverse - crown surrounded by rose wreath; incomplete date below - - by James Wyon.
B-9	NS-2	One Cent 186 - , bronze. Proof. Obverse - adopted (small bust) design by L.C. Wyon. Reverse - crown surrounded by rose wreath; incomplete date below - - by James Wyon.
B-13	NS-3	Half Cent 1861, bronze. Proof; dies ↑↑. As NS-1, except for the date. (National Currency Collection)

B-8	NS-4	One Cent 1861, bronze. Dies ↑↑; not a proof. As NS-2, except for the date. (National Currency Collection)

NOVA SCOTIA

BOWMAN NUMBERS	CHARLTON NUMBERS	
B-11	NS-5	

Half Cent 1861, bronze. Proof; dies ↑↓ . Obverse - large bust of Victoria by James Wyon. Reverse - pattern design as on NS-3. (National Currency Collection)

B-7 NS-6 One Cent 1861, bronze. Proof; dies ↑ ↑ . Obverse - large bust of Victoria by James Wyon. Reverse - pattern design as on NS-4. (National Currency Collection)

B-12 NS-7 Half Cent 1861, bronze. Proof; dies ↑ ↑ . Obverse - pattern design as on NS-5. Reverse - adopted design (Crown and date surrounded by a wreath of mayflowers and roses). (New Netherlands Coin Sale 1960)

B-10 NS-8 One Cent 1861, bronze. Proof; dies ↑ ↑ and ↑↓ . Obverse - pattern design as on NS-6. Reverse - adopted design (1861), large rose bud variety. (National Currency Collection)

B-10 NS-8a One Cent 1861, bronze. Proof; dies ↑ ↑ . As NS-8, except the reverse is the small rose bud variety (adopted design for 1861-1864).

NEW BRUNSWICK

PATTERNS

BOWMAN NUMBERS	CHARLTON NUMBERS	
B-15	NB-1	

B-15 NB-1 One Cent 1861, bronze. Proof; dies ↑ ↑. Obverse - large bust design by James Wyon as on NS-6, etc. Reverse - adopted design. (National Currency Collection)

B-20 NB-2 Ten Cents 1862, silver. Reeded edge proof; dies ↑ ↑. Obverse - adopted design. Reverse - legend and date surrounded by arabesque design somewhat similar to that later used for Newfoundland. (National Currency Collection)

TRIAL PIECES

NB-3 One Cent 1862, bronze. Proof. As adopted design, except for the date. Struck to make the date uniform for the 1862 proof sets.

OFFICIAL CONCOCTIONS

B-23 NB-4 Twenty Cents 1862, silver. Plain edge proof; dies ↑ ↑. Obverse - plain, except for the legend G.W. WYON/OBIT/MARCH 27TH 1862/AETAT/26 YEARS. Reverse - adopted design. This is an obituary medalet. (National Currency Collection)

B-18 NB-5 Five Cents 1870, silver. Reeded edge proof; dies ↑ ↑. Obverse - adopted design. Reverse - adopted design for the Dominion of Canada (wire rim variety). (National Currency Collection)

B-21 NB-6 Ten Cents 1870, silver. Reeded edge proof; dies ↑ ↑. Obverse - adopted design. Reverse - adopted design for the Dominion of Canada and New Brunswick. (National Currency Collection)

NEW BRUNSWICK

B-22   NB-7   Ten Cents 1871, silver. Reeded edge proof; dies ↑ ↑. As NB-6, except for the date. (Caldecott Sale 1912)

B-24   NB-8   Twenty Cents 1871, silver. Plain and reeded edge proofs; dies ↑ ↑. As the adopted design, except for the date. (National Currency Collection)

B-19   NB-9   Five Cents 1875, silver. Reeded edge proof; dies ↑ ↑. Obverse - adopted design. Reverse - adopted design for the Dominion of Canada. (National Currency Collection)

           NB-10   Five Cents 1875H, silver. Reeded edge proof. As NB-9, except for the H mint mark. (Douglas Robins 1974)

BRITISH COLUMBIA

PATTERNS

B-37   BC-1   Ten Dollars 1862, silver. Dies ↑↓. Obverse - crown and legend. Reverse - wreath, denomination and date. (National Currency Collection)

B-36   BC-2   Twenty Dollars 1862, silver. Dies ↑ ↑. Design similar to BC-1. (National Currency Collection)

B-37   BC-3   Ten Dollars 1862, gold. Design as BC-1. (B.C. Provincial Archives)

B-36   BC-4   Twenty Dollars 1862, gold. Design as BC-2. (B.C. Provincial Archives)

NEWFOUNDLAND

PATTERNS

BOWMAN NUMBERS	CHARLTON NUMBERS	
	NF-1	One Cent 1864. Reverse - similar to the design adopted for the New Brunswick cent. Presently unknown as a struck piece, but may exist.
B-28	NF-2	Five Cents 1864, bronze. Plain edge. Obverse - adopted design. Reverse - crown and wreath design adopted for New Brunswick, etc. (W.W.C. Wilson Sale 1925)
B-29	NF-3	Ten Cents 1864, bronze. Plain edge. Obverse - adopted design. Reverse - crown and wreath design adopted for New Brunswick, etc. (British Museum)

B-32	NF-4	Twenty Cents 1864, bronze. Indented corded edge; dies ↑↓. Obverse - adopted design. Reverse - crown and wreath design adopted for New Brunswick. (National Currency Collection)

B-31	NF-5	Two Dollars 1864, bronze. Plain edge; dies ↑↓. Obverse - adopted design. Reverse - crown and wreath from the New Brunswick, etc. ten cents with the legend TWO/DOLLARS/1864 in the centre. (National Currency Collection)

B-25	NF-6	One Cent, bronze. Dies ↑↑ ; not a proof. Obverse - similar to adopted design, except the legend reads VICTORIA QUEEN. Reverse - similar to adopted design, except one leaf is missing from the top of each side of the wreath. (National Currency Collection)

BOWMAN NUMBERS	CHARLTON NUMBERS	
B-27	NF-7	One Cent 1865, bronze. Proof; dies ↑↑. Obverse - adopted design for Nova Scotia and New Brunswick. Reverse - pattern designs as for NF-6, except for the date.

NF-8 Five Cents 1865, silver. Plain edge proof; dies ↑↓. Obverse - adopted design. Reverse - similar to the adopted design, except the arches are much thinner. (National Currency Collection)

NF-9 Ten Cents 1865, silver. Plain edge proof; dies ↑↓. Obverse - adopted design. Reverse - similar to the adopted design, except the arches are much thinner. (National Currency Collection)

NF-10 Twenty Cents 1865, silver. Plain edge proof; dies ↑↓. Obverse - adopted design. Reverse - similar to the adopted design, except the arches are much thinner. (National Currency Collection)

NF-11 Five Cents 1865, silver. Plain edge proof; dies ↑↓. Obverse - adopted design. Reverse - as the adopted design, except the arches and dots have raised line edges. (National Currency Collection)

NF-12   Ten Cents 1865, silver. Plain edge proof; dies ↑↓ . Obverse - adopted design. Reverse - as the adopted design, except the arches and dots have raised line edges. (National Currency Collection)

NF-13   Twenty Cents 1865, silver. Plain edge proof; dies ↑↓ . Obverse - adopted design. Reverse - similar to the adopted design, except for some details of the arches and the presence of a raised line just inside the rim denticles. (National Currency Collection)

B-33   NF-14   Two Dollars 1865, gold. Plain edge proof; dies ↑↑ . Obverse - adopted design. Reverse - similar to the adopted design, except the legend and date are in block type. (National Currency Collection)

B-34   NF-15   Two Dollars 1865, gold. Plain edge proof. Obverse - small bust of Victoria (from the five cents) in beaded circle with the legend VICTORIA D:G: REG:/NEWFOUNDLAND. Reverse - pattern design as on NF-14.

NF-16   Fifty Cents 1870, bronze. Plain edge proof; dies ↑↑ . Obverse - adopted design. Reverse - as the adopted design, except the denticles are longer and touch the device. (National Currency Collection)

NEWFOUNDLAND

BOWMAN NUMBERS	CHARLTON NUMBERS	
B-35	NF-17	Two Dollars 1870, gold. Plain edge proof. Obverse - pattern designs as on NF-15. Reverse - adopted design.

TRIAL PIECES

B-26	NF-18	One Cent 1864, bronze. Proof; dies ↑ ↑. As the adopted design, except for the date. (National Currency Collection)
	NF-19	Fifty Cents 1882, silver. Reeded edge proof. As the adopted design, except for the absence of the H mint mark. (British Museum)
	NF-20	Ten Cents 1945C, nickel. Struck on a thin blank; not a proof. (National Currency Collection)

DOMINION OF CANADA

PATTERNS

B-38	DC-1	One Cent 1876H, bronze. Proof; dies ↑ ↑. Obverse - adopted laureated head design for the Province of Canada. Reverse - adopted design. (National Currency Collection)

	DC-2	Ten Cents (no date), bronze. Reeded edge proof. Obverse - adopted design (Haxby Obv. 6). Reverse - plain, except for a "B" engraved on the piece after it was struck. Probably unique. (National Currency Collection)

BOWMAN NUMBERS	CHARLTON NUMBERS	

DC-3   Fifty Cents 1870, bronze. Plain edge proof; dies ↑ ↑. Obverse - no L.C.W. on the truncation, but otherwise very similar to Haxby Obv. 2. Reverse - slight differences in some leaves compared to the adopted design. (National Currency Collection)

DC-5   One Cent 1911, bronze. Specimen. As the adopted design for 1912-1920, except for the date; i.e. the obverse legend has DEI GRA:. (Royal Mint Collection)

B-40   DC-6   One Dollar 1911, silver. Reeded edge specimen; dies ↑ ↑. Obverse - the standard MacKennal design later adopted for the 1936 dollar. Reverse - crown, wreath, legend and date. (Douglas Robins 1976)

In the Dominion of Canada Currency Act of 1910, which received Royal Assent on the 4th of May, 1910, provision was made for the striking of a Canadian silver dollar. The schedule appended to the Act specified a coin of 360 grains weight and a standard fineness of .925 silver. The Dominion Government, having decided to add a silver dollar to the coinage, purchased a new coining-press from Taylor and Challen of Birmingham, England, for the express purpose of striking coins of this size. A pair of dies for the new coin were prepared by the Die and Medal Department of the Royal Mint, London, and at least two specimens were struck. When cases were prepared for the specimen sets of the first Canadian coinage of George V, a space was left for the dollar. Later, however, the Dominion authorities decided against the issue of a silver dollar at that time, although no reason was given for this decision.

Only two specimens of the 1911 silver dollar are known to exist; one is in the Royal Mint Museum and the other was recently purchased in a private sale for $135,000.00 (some of this information was obtained from the 1976 O.N.A. Auction Catalogue).

DOMINION OF CANADA

BOWMAN NUMBERS	CHARLTON NUMBERS	
	DC-6a	One Dollar 1911, lead. As DC-6, except for the metal. Probably unique. (National Currency Collection)

B-41	DC-7	Five Dollars 1911, gold. Reeded edge specimen; dies ↑ ↑. As the adopted design for 1912-1914, except for the date. (Royal Mint Collection)

B-42	DC-8	Ten Dollars 1911, gold. Reeded edge specimen; dies ↑ ↑. As the adopted design for 1912-1914, except for the date. (Royal Mint Museum)

	DC-9	Five Dollars 1928, bronze. Reeded edge; dies ↑ ↑. Obverse - as the adopted design for the 1912-1914 issues. Reverse - modified Canadian arms by G.E. Kruger-Gray. (National Currency Collection)

BOWMAN
NUMBERS

CHARLTON
NUMBERS

DC-10

Ten Dollars 1928, bronze. Reeded edge, dies ↑ ↑ . Obverse - as the adopted design for the 1912-1914 issues. Reverse - modified Canadian arms by G.E. Kruger-Gray. (National Currency Collection)

DC-11

Five Dollars 1928, bronze. Reeded edge. Obverse - planed off flat just inside the denticles after striking; SPECIMEN has been punched in by hand. Reverse - pattern design as on DC-9. The entire piece has been acid-etched (officially) giving it a light brown colour. (National Currency Collection)

DC-12

Ten Dollars 1928, bronze. Reeded edge. Obverse - planed off flat just inside the denticles after striking; SPECIMEN has been punched in by hand. Reverse - pattern design as on DC-10. The entire piece has been etched as for DC-11.

DC-13

One Dollar 1964, tin. Plain edge; not a proof. Obverse - blank, except for small symbol ⌐ . Reverse - similar to the adopted design, except for being higher in relief and having thin rounded rim denticles instead of wide square ones. Piefort, Unique. (National Currency Collection)

BOWMAN NUMBERS	CHARLTON NUMBERS	

DC-14   One Dollar 1967, silver. Reeded edge; not a specimen. Similar to the adopted design, except the fields on both sides are flat instead of concave and the rim beads differ slightly in size and position.

TRIAL PIECES

DC-15   Fifty Cents (no date), white metal. Trial impression of portrait of Victoria only; as on Haxby Obv. 2, 1870-1872. (National Currency Collection)

DC-16   One Cent 1876H, cupro-nickel. Proof. As the adopted design. (American Numismatic Society)

DC-17   One Cent 1876, bronze. Proof; dies↑ ↑ . As the adopted design, except for the absence of the H mint mark. (National Currency Collection)

DC-18   Five Cents 1875, silver. Reeded edge proof; dies ↑↓ . As the adopted design, except for the absence of the H mint mark. (National Currency Collection)

DC-19   One Cent 1937, brass. Specimen; dies ↑↓ . As the adopted design. Slightly thicker than normal. (National Currency Collection)

DC-20   Five Cents 1937, brass. Specimen; dies↑↓ . As the adopted design. Slightly thicker than normal. (National Currency Collection)

DC-21   Ten Cents 1937, brass. Reeded edge specimen; dies↑ ↓. As the adopted design. Slightly thicker than normal. (National Currency Collection)

DOMINION OF CANADA

DC-22   Twenty-Five Cents 1937, brass. Reeded edge specimen; dies ↑↓. As the adopted design. Slightly thicker than normal. (National Currency Collection)

DC-23   Fifty Cents 1937, brass. Reeded edge sepcimen; dies ↑↓. As the adopted design. Thicker than normal. (National Currency Collection)

DC-24   Twenty-Five Cents 1937, bronze. Reeded edge; dies ↑↑. As the adopted design. Normal thickness. (National Currency Collection)

DC-25   Five Cents 1942, nickel. Dies ↑↑; not a specimen. As the 12-sided design adopted for the tombac pieces. (National Currency Collection)

DC-26   One Cent 1943, copper-plated steel. Dies ↑↑; not a specimen. As the adopted design. (National Currency Collection)

DC-27   Five Cents 1943, steel. Specimen. As the design adopted for the tombac pieces. (Piece seen, but composition not confirmed).

DC-28   Five Cents 1944, tombac. As the design adopted for the chrome-plated steel pieces. (Piece seen, but composition not confirmed).

DC-29   Five Cents 1951, chrome-plated steel. Specimen; dies ↑↑. As the commemorative design struck in nickel (National Currency Collection)

DC-30   Five Cents 1952. Specimen; dies ↑↑. As the adopted design, except differs in composition, which has not yet been determined. White coloured, instead of the normal bluish. (National Currency Collection)

DC-31   Fifty Cents 1959, tin. Uniface on thick, oversize blank. Obverse - blank except for the engraved inscription (added after the piece was struck) FIRST TRIAL/Oct 27th/1958. Reverse - as the adopted design, except lacks rim denticles. Unique. (National Currency Collection)

DOMINION OF CANADA

OFFICIAL CONCOCTIONS

BOWMAN NUMBERS	CHARLTON NUMBERS	
	DC-32	Twenty Cents 1871, silver. Reeded and plain edge specimen; dies ↑ ↓ . As the adopted design for the Province of Canada, except for the date. (National Currency Collection)

	DC-33	(Fifty Cent Size) 1907, bronze. Reeded edge. Obverse - OTTAWA MINT/TRIAL RUN. Reverse - NOVEMBER/1907. Struck to adjust the presses prior to the production of the first coins. (National Currency Collection)

Canadian Silver Coins from 1908 have upright reverses (↑ ↑). Those dated before 1908 have upset or medal reverses (↑ ↓).

NUMISMATIC TERMS

ASSAY: The analytical test to determine the purity and weight of metal.

BAG MARKS: Slight scratches and nicks acquired by coins in contact with others in a mint bag. Most common on large and heavy silver and gold coins.

BLANKS: Flat, round metal discs or planchets from which the coins are made.

BROCKAGE: A coin with the same design raised on one side and incuse on the other, caused by a previously struck coin sticking in the die and striking another blank.

BULLION: Uncoined gold or silver in the form of bars, ingots and plates. Bullion value is a term used in reference to value of metal content in common and mutilated gold and silver coins.

BUSINESS STRIKE: Any coin struck with the intention of circulating as money.

CABINET FRICTION: The friction on uncirculated coins attributed to their storage in a collection.

CAMEO-EFFECT: A description of the appearance of certain gold and silver proof coins which have frosty devices on highly polished fields.

CARAT: The degree of fineness of gold. Pure gold is 24 carats and most gold coins have a fineness of 22 carats.

CLASHED DIES: Damaged dies caused by the absence of a planchet at the time of striking. Each die retains a portion of its opposite's design, in addition to its own. The resulting coins show a partial impression of the reverse design on the obverse and/or vice versa. Such marks will be referred to as clash marks.

CLEANED: A general term referring to cleaning a coin by any method. This often reduces the value and is not recommended.

COIN: A piece of metal with a distinctive design, a fixed value, a specific weight and diameter, which was issued by a government as money.

COLLAR: The part of the die which affixes to the edge of the planchet to prevent movement during striking. Reeded edge coins are made by having the collar grooved; 12 sided five cent nickels are made by having regular round blanks struck in a 12 sided collar.

COMMEMORATIVE: A coin issued to commemorate a special event or honour an outstanding person.

DEBASEMENT: Debasement of a coin takes place when the issuing authority reduces the purity of the metal, lowering the intrinsic value of the coin but circulating it at par with the previous coins of the original purity. This happened in Canada in 1968 when the silver content of coins for circulation was replaced entirely with nickel.

DENTICLES: The device used around the periphery of a coin to discourage counterfeiters.

DEVICE: Any design feature appearing on the obverse, reverse or edge of a coin.

DIADEMED: A coin where the portrait head has a headband or fillet as a sign of royalty.

DIE: Engraved metal pieces used to impress the design of a coin on a blank planchet.

DIE BULGE: A roundish, raised area on a coin caused by the swelling of a die.

DIE CRACK: A raised line appearing on a coin reflecting a stress crack which developed on the die.

DIE STRIATION: A series of fine, raised and nearly parallel lines resulting from extreme pressure used in the striking of a coin. Occasionally seen on well struck gem business strikes.

ESSAI: A trial piece from dies already accepted for regular coinage. It may bear a date or mint mark other than on the coins issued for circulation or it may be a different metal.

EXERGUE: The lower part of a coin or medal which is usually divided from the "field" by a line under which is contained the date, place of minting or engraver's initials.

FIELD: The open areas on either side of a coin not occupied by the portrait, design or inscription.

FIRST-STRIKE: A coin struck from new dies. Usually fully struck and frequently proof-like.

FLAN: The blank metal cut to shape but before receiving the die impression. Also called a planchet.

FULLY STRUCK: Refers to a coin on which all of the intended design is in evidence.

HAIRLINES: Minute lines or scratches sometimes visible on a coin, caused by cleaning or polishing.

HIGH POINTS: The highest points on the design of a coin. The first points to show wear.

IMPAIRED PROOF: A coin struck as a rpoof, but no longer in mint state.

INCUSE: Coins with either obverse or reverse design sunk below the coin's surface. A design raised above the surface is in relief.

NUMISMATIC TERMS

INGOT: A piece of precious metal shaped in a mould. Much of the gold reserves of various nations are stored in ingots and bars.

INTRINSIC: The intrinsic value of a coin is the actual metal value of the coin. Canadian silver coins before 1968 are worth more intrinsically than the face value, while the nickel 10¢, 25¢, 50¢ and $1 coin from 1968 to date are worth less intrinsically than the face value.

IRIDESCENT: A multi-coloured blending or toning, frequently found in older uncirculated coins.

LAMINATED PLANCHET: A "peeling off" of a top layer of the metal of a planchet.

LEGEND: The principal inscription on a coin.

MAJOR VARIETY: A coin of the same date, mint mark and denomination as another, but struck from another pair of dies and having at least the major device added, removed or redesigned.

MATTE PROOF: A proof coin for which the planchet is treated in a manner other than polishing. A dull and grainy finish is achieved.

MEDAL: A commemorative metal piece in honour of a person or event. Not money.

MEDALET: A small medal.

MINOR VARIETY: A coin of the same date, mint mark and denomination as another, but struck from a different pair of dies. Easily recognizable from the other, though all major devices are similar.

MINT ERROR: A misstruck or defective coin produced by a Mint.

MINT MARK: Letter designation for a branch mint product.

MOTTO: A phrase exemplifying an ideal or principle of a nation.

MULE: A coin struck from dies not designed to be used together.

OBVERSE: The "face-up" side of the coin, regarded as more important than the reverse side and usually bearing the portrait of the monarch.

OVERDATE: The date made by an engraver at the mint punching one or more numbers on a previously dated die.

OVERSTRIKE: A coin where part of the design, particularly the date, appears under another design or date.

PATINA: A green or brown surface film frequently found on ancient copper and bronze coins caused by oxidation over a long period of time. Also by moisture and certain soils.

PATTERN: A submitted design sample by engravers when a new coinage is comtemplated. If the design is adopted for regular coinage with the same date, the piece ceases to be a pattern. Patterns are usually struck as proofs.

PLANCHET: The metal disc from which a coin is made.

PLANCHET FLAKE: A geometrically shaped depressed area of a coin which occurred in preparation of the planchet.

PLANCHET DEFECT: The general terms for any of several types of imperfections on a planchet.

PRESENTATION PIECE: A coin which was struck for a purpose other than to circulate or to sell to the public; similar to a proof.

PROOF: Coins struck for collectors and using specially polished or otherwise prepared dies.

PROOF-LIKE: A business strike having some characteristics of a proof. Often struck from proof dies before the polish has completely worn off. Sometimes occurs from repolishing of dies. Proof-likes are most like proofs in terms of their mirror-like refractive qualities.

PROOF ONLY: A statement which expresses the fact that no business strikes were made for an issue.

REEDING: The graining or milling which appears on the edges of many coins.

RELIEF: A relief design is one where the lettering and design is raised above the surface of the coin.

RESTRIKE: Any coin struck later than the date appearing on the coin.

REVERSE: Opposite from obverse. The back or "tails" side of a coin.

ROTATED DIE: Dies are positioned and locked on a coining press by means of a key. When these keys come loose, rotation can occur resulting in the next coin being struck with the obverse and reverse dies rotated. Coins struck from rotated dies are error.

In compiling this catalogue, the author, a recognized authority on Canadian numismatics and a professional numismatist for over 25 years, has augmented his own knowledge and research with the experience and suggestions of many of the best known and eminently qualified numismatists, whose names appear on the panel of contributors.

This book provides the most complete, comprehensive and authoritative coverage of Canada's coins from 1858 to the present. Up to the minute information and valuations, excellent photographs, and grading guide make it the most widely used reference book in its field.

The catalogue belongs on the shelf of all collectors interested in Canadian numismatics. It will be a useful reference for historians, librairies, banks and schools.

Coin shown twice actual size.